MAJOR SCALE
MASTER

118 Warm-ups to Revolutionize Your Guitar Playing

The **Missing Method**

An imprint of
Tenterhook Books, LLC
Akron, Ohio

Christian J. Triola

The Missing Method

Discover what you've been missing.

Bulk sales inquiries can be directed to the author at info@themissingmethod.com.

Cover and Book Design by Amy Joy, ©2020 Amy Joy

The Missing Method™ for Guitar is an imprint of Tenterhook Books, LLC. The Missing Method name and logos are property of Tenterhook Books, LLC.

First Edition 2020, Tenterhook Books, LLC. Akron, Ohio.

Library of Congress Control Number: 2020922919

ISBN-13: 978-1-953101-17-4

Table of Contents

About the Author i

    What is the Missing Method? i

Introduction. 1

    How this Book Works 1

    Overview & Recommended Approach 2

Basic Techniques 3

    How to hold the pick. 3

    Fret Hand Technique **4**

Unit 1: Major Scale Basics 6

    The C Major Scale 8

Unit 2: Moving Beyond the Basic Pattern 18

    C Major Licks 30

    Arpeggios in the Key of C Major. 32

    Arpeggio Exercises 32

Unit 3: Pattern 2 Moving Up the Neck 36

    C Major Licks 51

    Arpeggio Exercises 53

Unit 4: Pattern 3 Moving Up the Neck 58

    Arpeggio Exercises .72

    Major Scale Licks 75

    Connecting Patterns .77

Unit 5: Pattern 4 .80

    Arpeggio Exercises 93

    Major Scale Licks 96

    Connecting Patterns 98

Unit 6: Pattern 5 102

    Arpeggio Exercises 115

    Connecting Patterns 121

Unit 7: Pattern 1 Up an Octave 126

Arpeggio Exercise. 132

Major Scale Licks 133

Unit 8: The Three Notes Per String Approach 136

Arpeggio Exercise. 144

Major Scale Licks 146

Arpeggio Exercise. 155

Major Scale Licks 157

Unit 9: How to Change keys 160

Changing from C Major to G Major 161

All G Major Scale Patterns 162

Example Key Change Warm-Ups 163

What's Next? 164

Root Finder Chart 165

Appendix 167

How to Tune Your Guitar 168

Guitar Tuners and Other Tuning Resources 170

How to Read Tablature 171

The Elements of Reading Music 172

The Staff 172

Ledger Lines 173

Understanding Time 173

Eighth Notes 175

Sixteenth Notes. 175

Keeping Time: How to Use Your Metronome 176

Quick Reference Scale Charts 178

Three Notes Per String 179

Resources to Help You Take Your Playing Further . . 180

About the Author

Over the past 20 years, Christian J. Triola has taught hundreds of students to play guitar and authored over two dozen popular guitar method books. He holds a Master's Degree in Education and a Bachelor's Degree in Music (Jazz Studies), and has played in a variety of bands in addition to his many solo performances.

What is the Missing Method?

The Missing Method™ is an imprint of Tenterhook Books, LLC, owned and operated by Christian J. Triola and his wife, Amy Joy Triola. The imprint began in 2013 in an effort to bring method books that didn't exist to Christian's guitar students. Today, we have expanded that mission to create high quality instructional materials to inspire and empower guitar players around the world. The Missing Method now spans many series of guitar books, addressing topics from chords, to note reading, practice strategies, playing techniques and much more.

Learn more and join our growing community at TheMissingMethod.com.

Welcome to
The Missing Method for Guitar community!

We're dedicated to helping you master your instrument. To that end, there are a couple of resources we want to make sure you are aware of:

The Missing Method for Guitar YouTube channel.

Here you'll find free weekly lessons we know you'll find useful as you work your way through this book, including tutorials on how to play your favorite songs. Find it at: https://bit.ly/Missing-Method-YouTube.

The Missing Method for Guitar Monthly Newsletter.

We only send out one a month, and you won't want to miss the updates on new resources, discount promotions, and more. Plus, when you sign up, we'll send you a free ebook full of exercises to help improve your playing. Sign up at https://themissingmethod.com/newsletter/.

Introduction

The major scale is a pleasant-sounding arrangement of whole steps and half steps that give any musician or composer a variety of seemingly endless combinations from which to express themselves. It's the foundational scale in western music from which all other scales are compared and derived. It's classic sound was made famous by the movie, *The Sound of Music,* where the kids sing, "Do, Re, Mi, Fa, Sol, La, Ti, Do..." And it is the basis for learning all types of music, from classical, to rock, to country, to jazz, to just about anything you can think of. This scale is so much a part of our culture that its foundations can be traced back to the ancient Greeks. But they were only the first to write it down and make sense of it, which means there's a good chance it was around long before that!

And now it's your turn. Mastering the major scale is a skill that all musicians need to have. Once you know it, all other scales make a lot more sense. You can compose with it, recognize it in songs to learn them faster, and use it to improvise. For guitar players, the pentatonic scale is often the scale we learn first, but for the rest of the musical world, it's the major scale. And once you know the pentatonic scale, the major scale simply adds two more notes to complete its sound, but in doing so it creates new challenges. Therefore, the major scale is the logical next step in developing both your ear and your guitar technique.

How this Book Works

Major Scale Master is designed to help you continue to both develop your fret-hand and pick-hand techniques while you learn the major scale all over the fretboard. Each unit takes you through a different area of the neck, teaching you how to play the major scale from its root. Then it goes on to include all diatonic notes in that area of the neck (diatonic meaning "in the key") until the whole fretboard is covered. In later units, you'll learn how to approach the major scale using the three-notes-per-string method, how to connect scale patterns together, and how to change keys easily. Each section also includes a series of arpeggios to learn, as well as licks to help you better understand how the major scale can be applied to the guitar.

Overview & Recommended Approach

Be sure to practice every single warm-up and lick in this book with a metronome. If you've successfully completed The Missing Method™'s *Technique Master* or *Pentatonic Master*, then I'm sure you are already very familiar with how to use a metronome. However, if you don't have much metronome experience, a section on how to use a metronome is included in every book in the Technique Master series, including this one. You'll find it in the appendix. Like everything having to do with music, it takes time and practice to get comfortable using a metronome, but it is well worth the momentary discomfort. Don't give up on the metronome!

Next, I'd also recommend humming or singing each exercise in this book as you learn them. That way you will be able to connect your ear to what your fingers are doing. You are essentially internalizing the sound, which will help you develop your overall musicianship. You don't have to be a good singer; you just have to vocalize the pitches to help you better understand them.

Final note: don't neglect your tuning. Always check your tuning before playing your guitar. This may seem like an obvious thing to mention, but not all guitar players pay attention to this vital detail. Again, if you need help with this, guidance can be found in the Appendix. You can also find video tutorials on tuning on our YouTube channel: https://bit.ly/Missing-Method-YouTube.

So good luck, pay close attention to detail, and don't forget to use your metronome!

Basic Techniques

How to hold the pick

1 First, curve the fingers of your picking hand inward, while keeping them relaxed. Don't make a fist.

2 Second, place the pick on top of the first knuckle, so that the point of the pick faces outward.

3 Third, place your thumb over the pick to hold it in place. This may feel awkward or uncomfortable at first, but once you get used to it, you'll have full control over the pick.

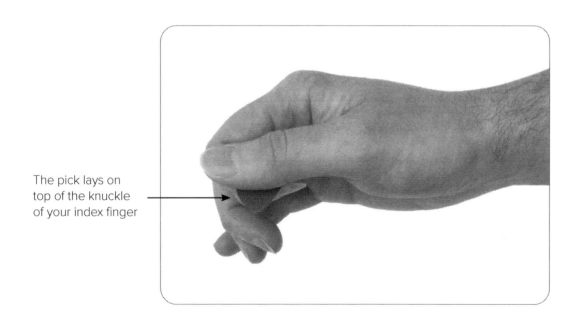

The pick lays on top of the knuckle of your index finger

Fret Hand Technique

Proper fret hand technique is crucial to getting a good sound and avoiding injury.

1 First, always keep your fingers up on their tips. The fingers should be spread apart and not touching each other.

2 Second, the wrist should be dropped down and the thumb planted behind the neck so that the thumb falls between the first and second fingers when looking at it from above.

3 Third, the knuckles of your hand should be running completely parallel to the neck, and the palm of your hand should not make contact with the neck.

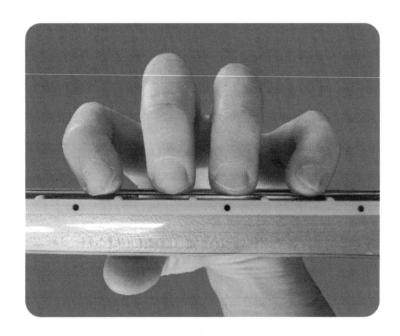

Unit 1

Major Scale Basics

Unit 1: Major Scale Basics

The major scale is a collection of pitches that is the starting point for understanding a great deal of music theory. It is often taught to prepare musicians to learn music faster. But the question remains: what is it?

The **major scale** is simply the resulting sound of a specific set of whole steps and half steps arranged in a progressive order, from low to high. Think of this set of whole steps and half steps like a formula, which produces a familiar sound:

Whole   Whole   Half   Whole   Whole   Whole   Half

For the purposes of this book, we will be using the key of C because it contains no sharps or flats. This will enable you to learn the basic major scale all over the neck using a variety of warm-ups, licks, and arpeggio exercises. Once you can do that, then other keys can be applied to the same warm-ups, which is explained further in Unit 9.

Using C as our starting point, let's take a look at how it fits with our formula.

W = Whole Step

H = Half Step

When you listen to these notes played in this order, the resulting sound is the major scale. Another way to think of it is to use the syllables taught in the movie, *The Sound of Music*: Do, Re, Mi, Fa, Sol, La, Ti, Do (otherwise known as **solfege** syllables).

In this book, we will be learning to master the major scale pattern all over the guitar neck. In Unit 1, we will begin by learning the C major scale in root position. (The *root* simply means the primary pitch of the scale.) To do this, the first set of warm-ups will focus on C major in the open position.

How to Play Warm-Up #1

1 To begin, simply try out the warm-up slowly. For now, don't worry about fingerings. Just play it and listen to the sound of it.

2 Next, work out the fingering:

- Play all notes on the third fret with the third finger.

- Play all notes on the second fret with the second finger.

- Play all first fret notes with the first finger.

3 Sync up with your metronome. Set the metronome to about 60 bpm (beats per minute). Then tap your foot along with the click. Once you have a feel for the beat, begin playing the major scale in sync with the click, giving each note a full beat.

Once you can play it perfectly, begin to increase the speed by 5 or 10 clicks (65 to 70bpm, for example). Tap your foot again to get in sync with the new speed, then play the scale. Continue doing this until you reach about 120 to 130bpm. You can always push your speed past this point once 130 becomes too easy.

The C Major Scale

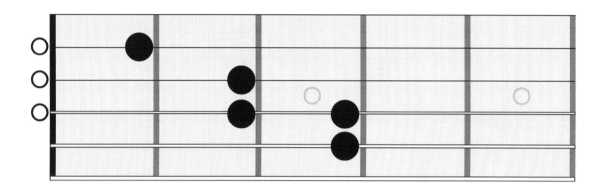

Warm-Up #1

How to Play Warm-Up #2

For warm-up number 2, the fingerings remain the same. However, we are now playing the notes as eighth notes, meaning that you now will be playing two notes per click of the metronome. Play the first half of each beat along with the click, then play the second half of each beat directly in between clicks. Again, start with 60bpm and work your way up to around 120 or 130.

Warm-Up #2

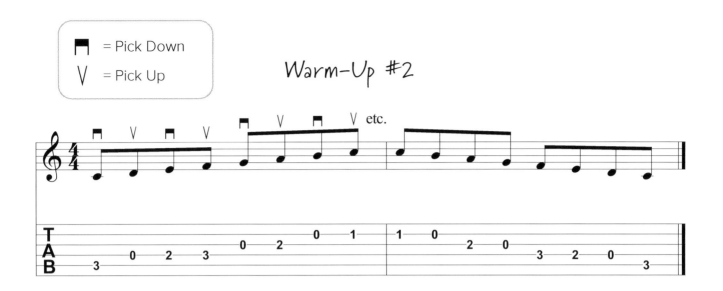

How to Play Warm-Up #3

For warm-up number 3, again the fingering remains the same. This time, however, we have moved on to sixteenth notes. This means that you will now play four even notes per click of the metronome. Make sure to keep your fingers and picking hand relaxed, and even though sixteenth notes are faster, don't rush them. Keep them controlled and even.

To play sixteenth notes, pick down on the first note in each set of sixteenths, then pick up for the next note, then down at the half-way point between clicks, then up again before the next click. Since these are faster, you may want to start slower than 60bpm and only work up to 115 to 120bpm.

Warm-Up #3

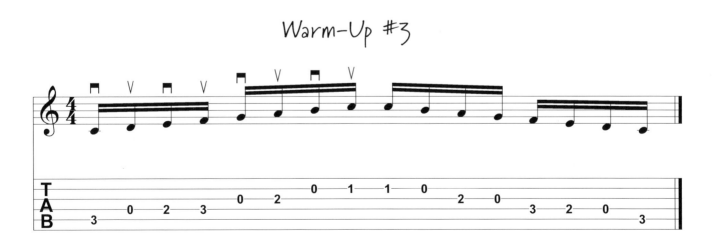

How to Play Warm-Up #4

Now that we've played through the C major scale in a linear fashion, we will now mix things up. Instead of playing directly through the scale, for this next warm-up, you will be playing the scale in thirds. So you will start with the root of the scale, then play the note three notes away, which is the "E" note in the key of C. Then you'll move back to "D", and then play three notes away from that (which is "F"), and so on until you reach the octave. At that point, you will play the same scale pattern descending.

Once again, the fingering will remain the same, and make sure to start slowly (60bpm) and move up to a more moderate tempo (130bpm).

Warm-Up #4

How to Play Warm-Up #5

For warm-up #5, the same pattern of thirds continues, but this time you'll be playing them as eighth notes. As a reminder, be sure to alternate your picking so that your pick goes down on the beat and up on the off-beats.

Once again, the fingering will remain the same, and make sure to start slowly (60bpm) and move up to a more moderate tempo (130bpm).

Warm-Up #5

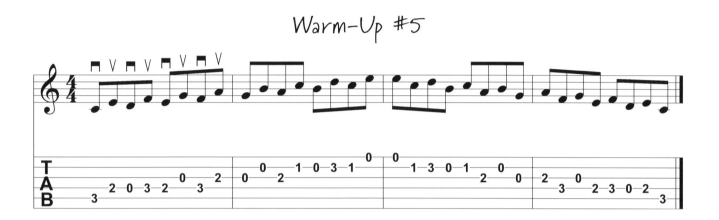

How to Play Warm-Up #6

Warm-up #6 is the same as #4 and #5, but this time with sixteenth notes. Just as before, make sure you alternate your picking as indicated.

The fingering remains the same. Make sure to start slowy (60bpm) and move up in increments of 5 to 10 until you arrive at a more moderate tempo (120bpm).

Warm-Up #6

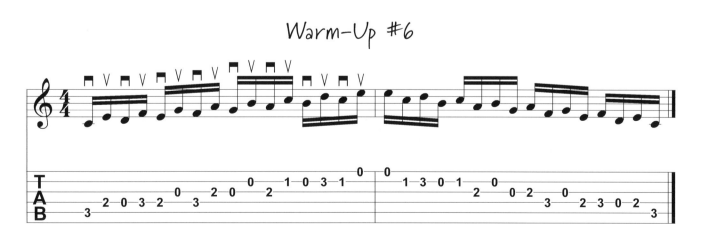

How to Play Warm-Ups #7, #8, and #9

The next set of warm-ups will have you playing the same scale, but this time in fourths. For example, the first note "C" will now move directly to "F". Then it will come back to "D" and then up four notes to "G" and so on, until each note of the scale has moved up a fourth. The same thing will happen descending.

Like before, each new warm-up will divide the beat differently, i.e. quarter notes, eighth notes, sixteenth notes.

As before, start off slowly. For this set of warm-ups, you may want to start at 50bpm before working up to speed. And again, try to get to at least 120bpm before moving on to the next warm-up.

Warm-Up #7

Warm-Up #8

Warm-Up #9

How to Play Warm-Ups #10, #11, and #12

These next three warm-ups have you practicing the major scale, but this time in fifths, meaning every five notes. For example, starting with the note "C", five notes from that is "G". This pattern continues until every note in the major scale has gone up a fifth. After that, the same pattern then descends in the same manner.

Much like the previous warm-ups, these warm-ups include quarter notes, eighth notes, and sixteenth notes.

Since fifths are bigger intervals, and harder to grab than some of the other intervals, be sure to go slower on this one. Start at about 50bpm and move up to 116bpm. Once comfortable, increase your speed to see how fast you can play it.

Warm-Up #10

Warm-Up #11

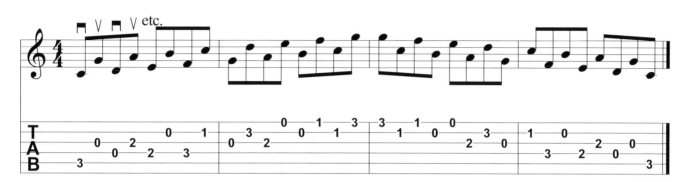

Warm-Up #12

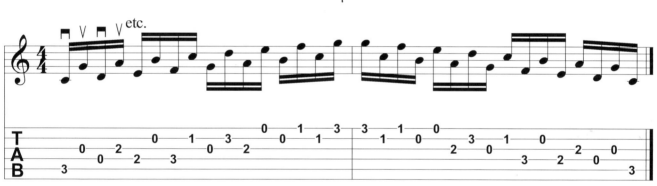

How to Play Warm-Up #13

Warm-up #13 gives you the opportunity to practice triplet rhythms while approaching the major scale in yet another way. This time we will travel up three notes, then back one, up three, back one all the way up the scale and back again.

Be sure to continue using the same fingering. Start the metronome at 50bpm, play the warm-up, and then begin increasing speed by intervals of 5 to 10 until you can play it around 110bpm.

Warm-Up #13

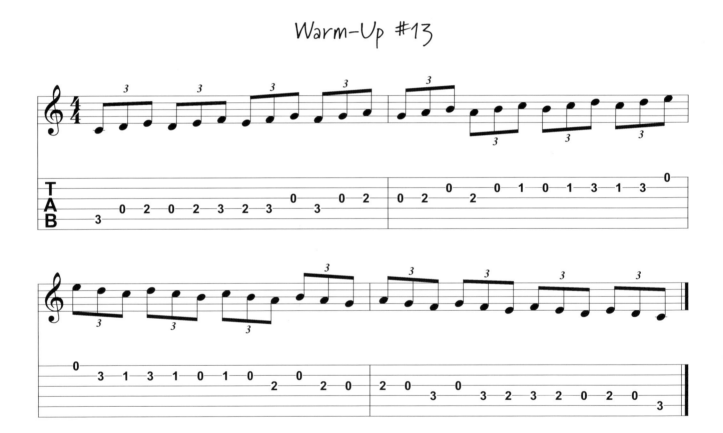

16

Unit 2

Beyond Basic

Unit 2: Moving Beyond the Basic Pattern

Use the following chart to play the C major scale with the warm-ups found in this unit. The gray circles show you where the note "C" is found. The black dots indicate scale tones. The white circles at the top of the chart indicate open strings. Start with the lowest string (bottom of the chart) and play each dot in turn.

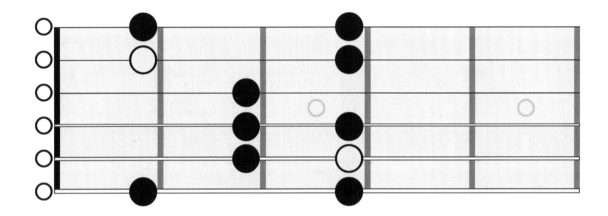

How to Play Warm-Up #14

Since the last unit showed you how to play the basic scale pattern, this one will expand on it. Therefore, you will begin this unit by playing through the entire set of notes found in C major, starting with the note "C" from last unit, continuing up to the octave, past one octave to include diatonic notes from the key of C, and back down past the low C to include additional key of C notes found in the same area of the neck.

The fingering is the same as the last unit, where all first fret notes are played with the index finger. All the second fret notes are played with the second finger. And all third fret notes are played with the third finger.

Start the warm-up at 60bpm and work your way up in increments of 5 to 10 until you can play it comfortably at 130bpm.

Warm-Up #14

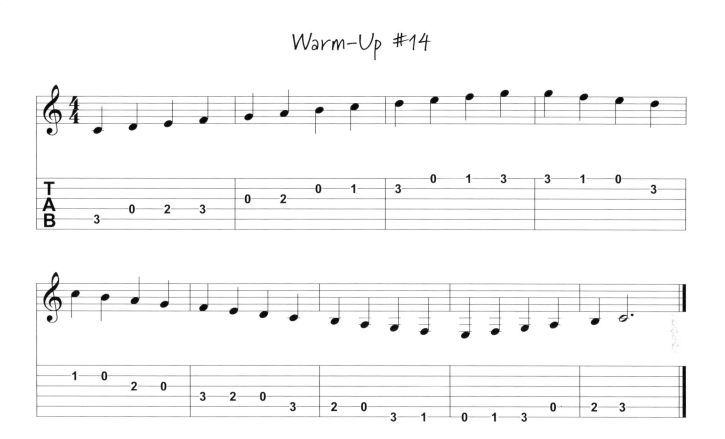

How to Play Warm-Up #15

Warm-up #15 takes a guitar-centered approach to learning the major scale. Instead of starting on the root of the scale, we are now starting on the lowest available note from that scale in this position, working our way to the highest note, and then back again, ultimately returning to the root note ("C") in order to resolve the sound.

The fingering is the same as Warm-up #14.

Start the warm-up at 60bpm and work your way up in increments of 5 to 10 until you can play it comfortably at 130bpm.

Warm-Up #15

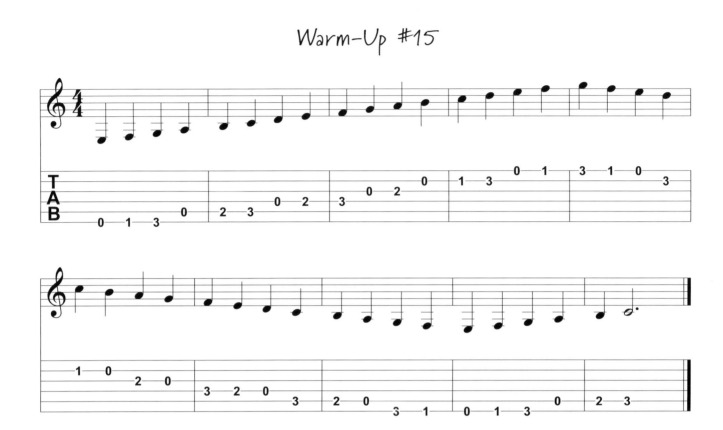

How to Play Warm-Up #16

Warm-up #16 returns to the C major scale starting on its root note, much like Warm-up #14. However, this time you will be playing it using eighth notes. Be sure to alternate your pick as you play through it, picking down on the downbeat and up on the up-beats.

The fingering is the same as Warm-up #14.

Start the warm-up at 60bpm and work your way up in increments of 5 to 10 until you can play it comfortably at 120bpm.

Warm-Up #16

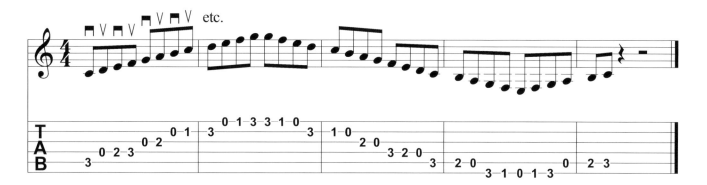

How to Play Warm-Up #17

Warm-up #17 divides the beat into sixteenth notes using the same set of notes found in the previous exercise.

The fingering is also the same as Warm-up #16.

Start the warm-up at 60bpm and work your way up in increments of 5 to 10 until you can play it comfortably at 120bpm.

Warm-Up #17

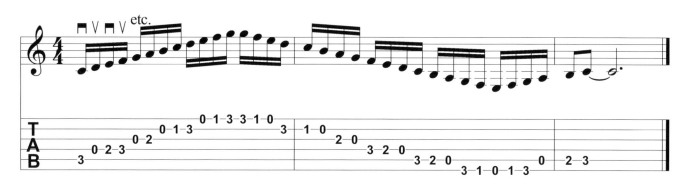

How to Play Warm-Ups #18, #19, and #20

The next three warm-ups move through the C major scale in thirds, meaning it starts with the root, skips the second note, plays the third note, then returns to the skipped note. From there it moves up a third again, and so on.

Once again the fingerings for these exercises remain the same. (See How to Play Warm-Up #14.)

Start each warm-up at 60bpm and gradually work up to around 120-130bpm.

Warm-Up #18

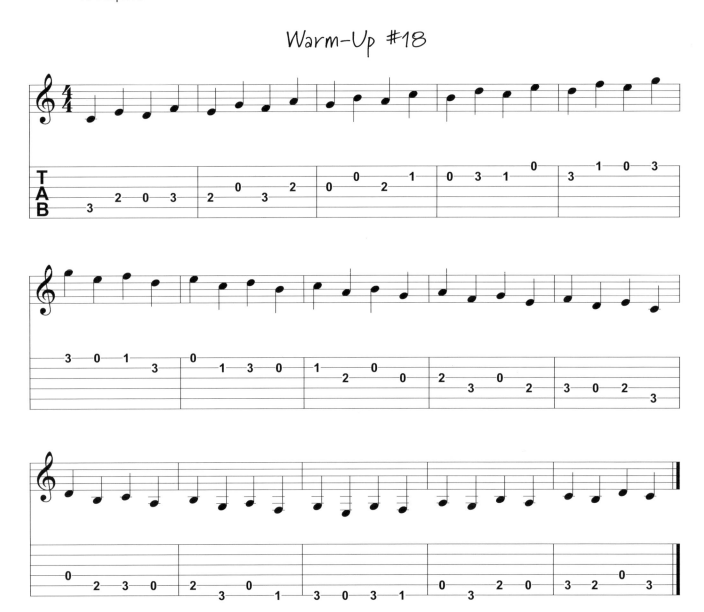

22

Warm-Up #19

Warm-Up #20

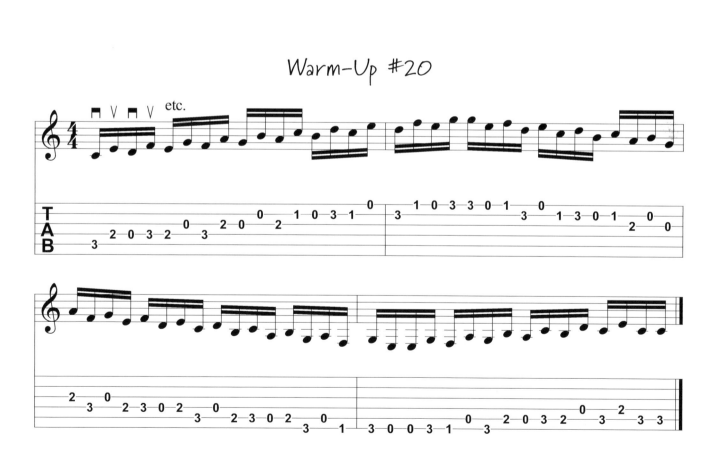

How to Play Warm-Ups #21, #22, and #23

The next three warm-ups move through the C major scale in fourths, meaning it starts with the root, skips the second note, plays the fourth note of the scale, then returns to the skipped note. From there it moves up a fourth again, and so on.

Once again the fingerings for the following three exercises remain the same. (See How to Play Warm-Up #14.)

Start each warm-up at 60bpm and gradually work up to around 120-130bpm.

Warm-Up #21

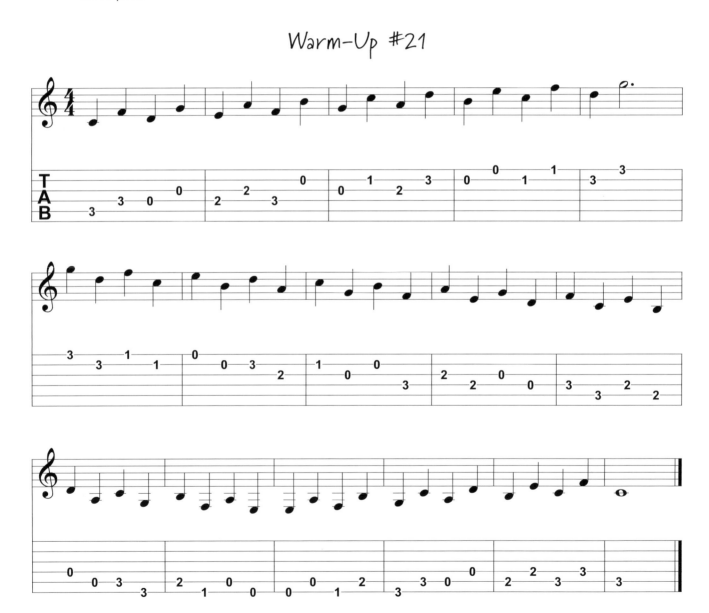

Warm-Up #22

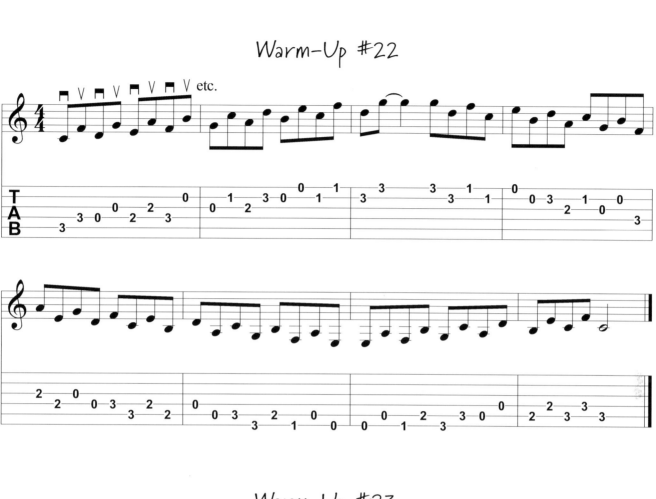

Warm-Up #23

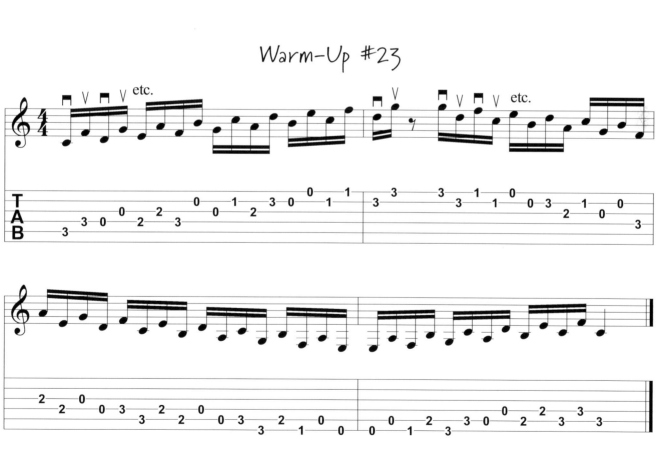

How to Play Warm-Ups #24, #25, and #26

The next three warm-ups move through the C major scale in fifths, meaning it starts with the root, skips the second note, plays the fifth note of the scale, then returns to the skipped note. From there it moves up five notes again, and so on.

Once again the fingerings for the following three exercises remain the same. (See How to Play Warm-Up #14.)

Start each warm-up at 60bpm and gradually work up to around 120-130bpm.

Warm-Up #24

Warm-Up #24 (continued)

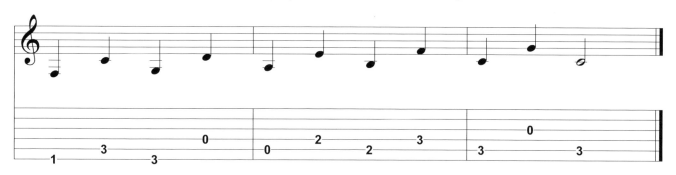

Warm-Up #25

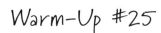

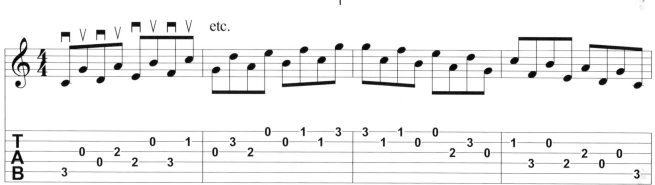

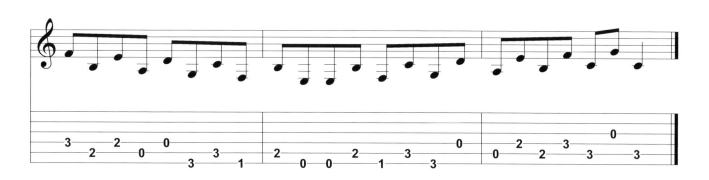

27

Warm-Up #26

How to Play Warm-Up #27

The following warm-up moves into triplets. However, rather than playing the scale directly in triplets, it moves up three notes and then moves one note back, then moves up three more, then back, and continues on until all the notes in C major are played. Keep in mind that for each set of triplets the metronome will click one time so that there are three even notes per beat.

Once again the fingerings for the following warm-up remain the same. (See How to Play Warm-Up #14.)

Begin by setting the metronome at 60bpm and gradually work up to around 120-130bpm.

Warm-Up #27

C Major Licks

This section of the unit takes the major scale and shows you how to use it as small musical phrases called **licks**. That way you can practice the scale in a more musical fashion, rather than simply playing through the scale in a predetermined order.

The fingerings for the following licks remain the same. (See How to Play Warm-Up #14.)

Begin by setting the metronome at 60bpm and gradually work up to around 120-130bpm for each lick.

Lick #1

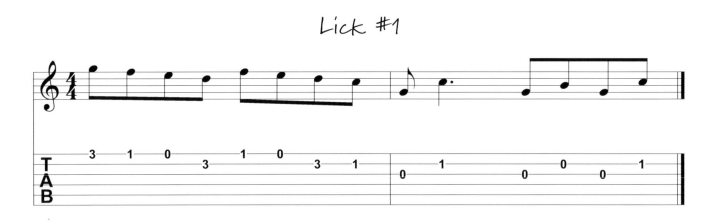

Lick #2

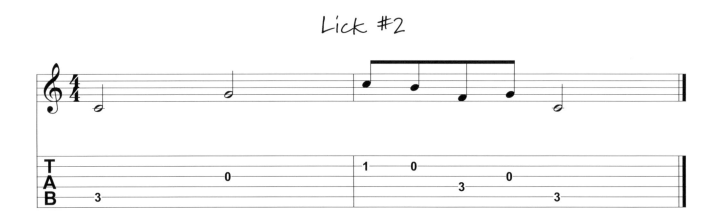

Lick #3

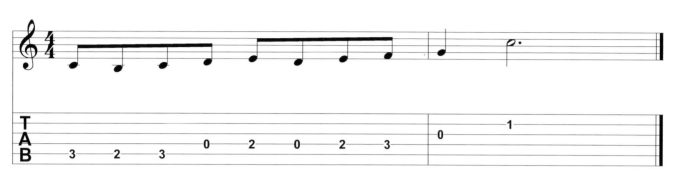

Lick #4

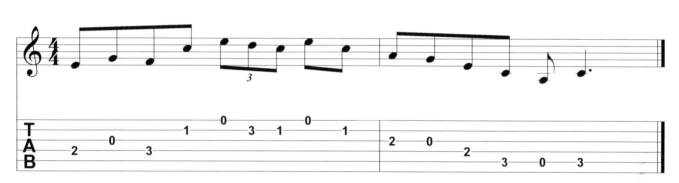

Lick #5

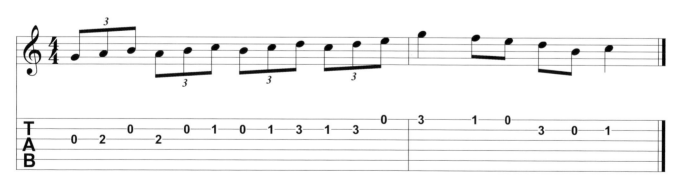

31

Arpeggio Exercises

For the following exercises, you will be playing all the arpeggios found within the C major scale. An **arpeggio** is simply a chord played one note at a time. In any major scale, the chords built off the first, fourth, and fifth notes are major chords, and the chords built off the second, third, and sixth notes are minor chords. The seventh note of the scale, when harmonized becomes a diminished chord. As you play through these arpeggios, be sure to listen for these three different arpeggio sounds.

The fingering for these exercises remains the same as all the other warm-ups found in this unit.

Continue to use your metronome with these exercises. Start off slowly, around 60bpm, and gradually build up speed until you can play these easily around 120bpm.

Arpeggios in the Key of C Major

Chord Name	Chord Symbol	Notes Found the Chord
C Major	C	C E G
D Minor	Dm	D F A
E Minor	Em	E G B
F Major	F	F A C
G Major	G	G B D
A Minor	Am	A C E
B Diminished	B dim	B D F

Arpeggio Exercise #1

Arpeggio Exercise #2

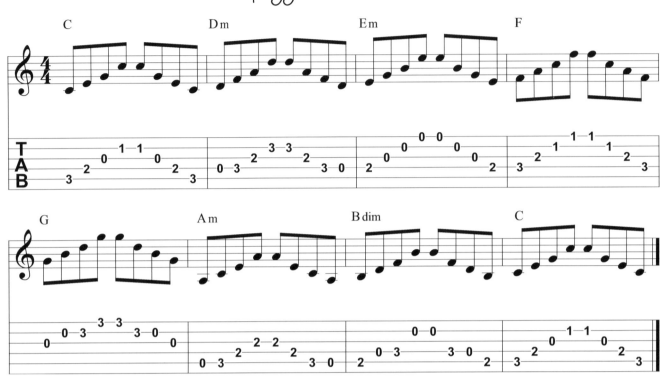

Arpeggio Exercise #3

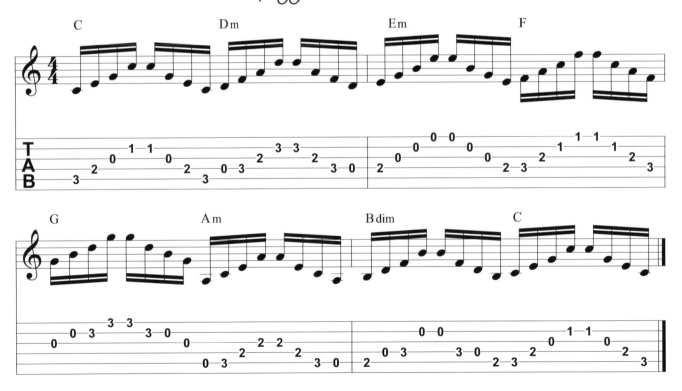

Unit 3

Pattern 2

Unit 3: Pattern 2 Moving Up the Neck

Use the following chart to play the C major scale with the warm-ups found in this unit. The gray circles show you where the note "C" is found. The black dots indicate scale tones. Start with the lowest string (bottom of the chart) and play each dot in turn, starting with the third fret of string six, then playing the fifth fret of string six, and so on.

Notice that the pattern starts on the third fret of the last string. Since this is the case, the fingering for this pattern is different from the last two units. Here, you'll start with the middle finger playing any note located on the third fret. The index finger covers the second fret, and the ring finger plays the third fret. Finally, the pinky is used on the fifth fret notes. However, there is a shift up on the second string, meaning that on that string, your index finger will play the third fret, your ring finger the fifth, and your pinky the sixth. Then to keep things consistent, when playing the first string, you'll use the index finger on fret three, and your ring finger on fret five. (See chart on the next page.)

When descending through the scale, you'll simply use the same fingerings, but in reverse.

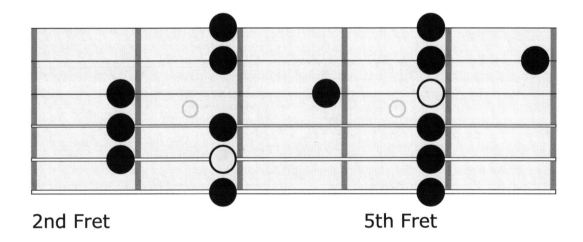

2nd Fret   5th Fret

36

How to Play Warm-Up #28

In this unit, we start to move the major scale up the neck into second position. (Positions are usually marked by where your first finger is playing.) For Warm-Up #28, you will play through the C major scale starting on the lowest "C" in the pattern and only playing up to the highest "C". This means there will be three strings left unplayed.

Start the warm-up at 60bpm and work your way up in increments of 5 to 10 until you can play it comfortably at 130bpm. Try to push yourself further once 130bpm feels too easy.

The fingerings for strings 3-6:

- Fret 2: Use the index finger (Finger 1)
- Fret 3: Use the middle finger (Finger 2)
- Fret 4: Use the ring finger (Finger 3)
- Fret 5: Use the pinky finger (Finger 4)

For strings 1 and 2:

- Fret 3: Use the index finger (Finger 1)
- Fret 5: Use the ring finger (Finger 3)
- Fret 6: Use the pinky finger (Finger 4)

Warm-Up #28

How to Play Warm-Ups #29 and #30

The next two warm-ups move through the basic C major scale using eighth notes and then in Warm-Up #30, sixteenth notes.

Once again the fingerings for the following exercises remain the same. (See Chart: How to Play Warm-Up #28.)

Start each warm-up at 60bpm and gradually work up to around 120-130bpm.

Warm-Up #29

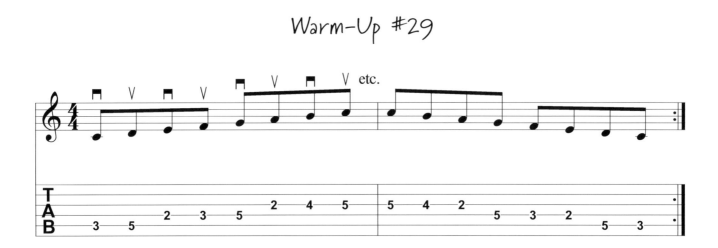

Warm-Up #30

How to Play Warm-Ups #31, #32, and #33

For the next three warm-ups, instead of simply playing the C major scale from its root, we are now going to expand it to include the surrounding notes that are also in the key. We will start on the root, move up to the octave, past the octave to grab notes from the next octave of the scale, then move back down to the root. Then we'll go lower than the root to get all the available notes in that position, and finally move back to the root.

Once again the fingerings for the following exercises remain the same. (See Chart: How to Play Warm-Up #28.)

Start each warm-up at 60bpm and gradually work up to around 120-130bpm.

Warm-Up #31

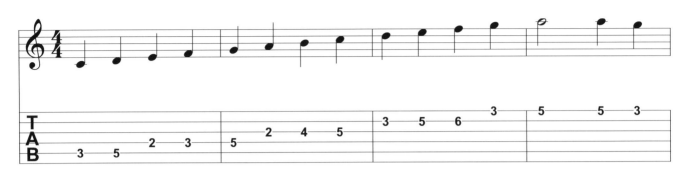

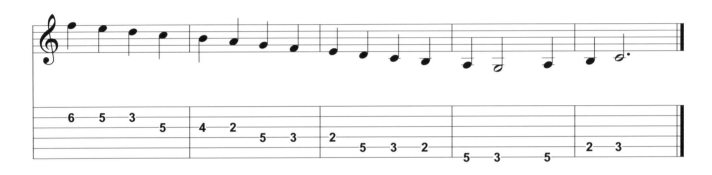

Warm-Up #32

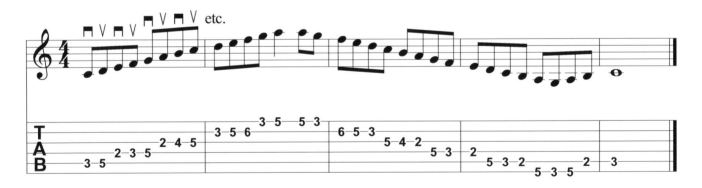

40

Warm-Up #33

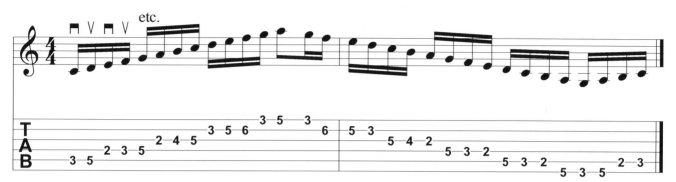

How to Play Warm-Ups #34, #35, and #36

The next three warm-ups move through the C major scale in thirds, starting with the root, skipping the second note, playing the third note, then returning to the note that was skipped. From there it moves up a third again, and so on.

Warm-Up #34 gives you quarter note rhythms to practice. Number 35 gives you eighth notes, and finally, sixteenth notes are utilized in Warm-Up #36.

Again, the fingerings for the following exercises remain the same. (See Chart: How to Play Warm-Up #28.)

Start each warm-up at 60bpm and gradually work up to around 120-130bpm.

Warm-Up #34

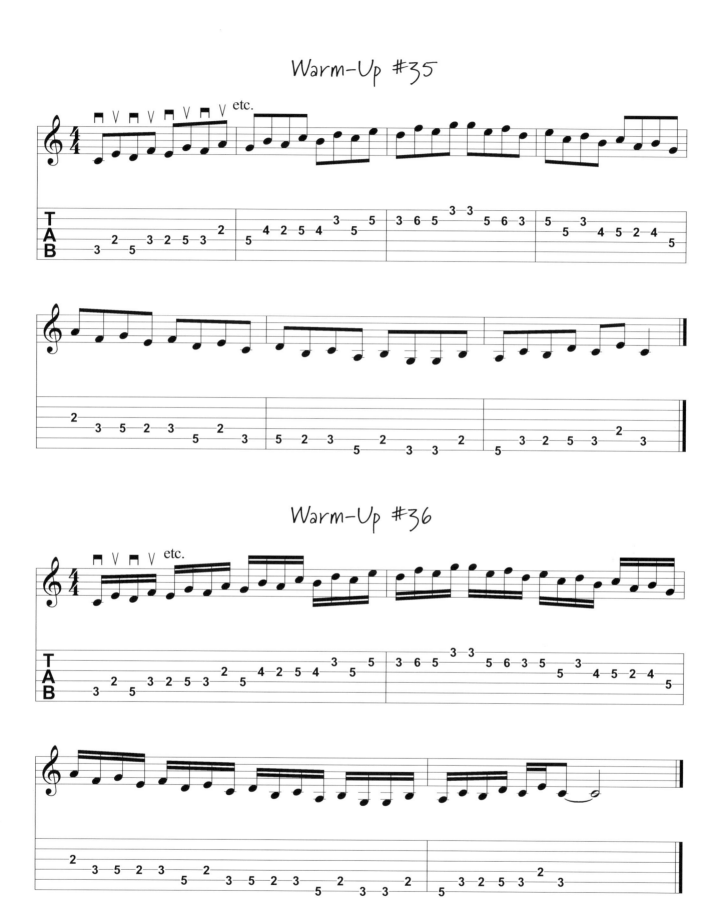

How to Play Warm-Ups #37, #38, and #39

The next three warm-ups move through the C major scale in fourths, starting with the root, skipping the second note, playing the fourth note of the scale, then returning to the note that was skipped. From there it moves up four notes again, and so on.

Warm-Up #37 gives you quarter note rhythms to practice. Number 38 gives you eighth notes to practice, and finally, sixteenth notes are utilized in Warm-Up #39.

Again, the fingerings for the following exercises remain the same. (See Chart: How to Play Warm-Up #28.)

Start each warm-up at 60bpm on your metronome and gradually work up to around 120 or 130bpm.

Warm-Up #37

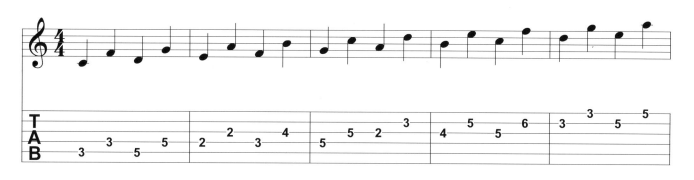

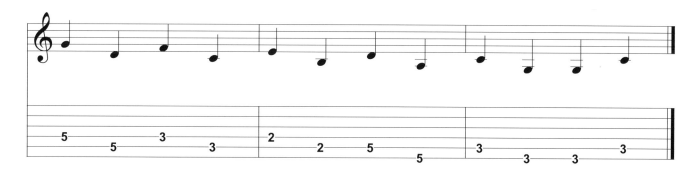

45

Warm-Up #38

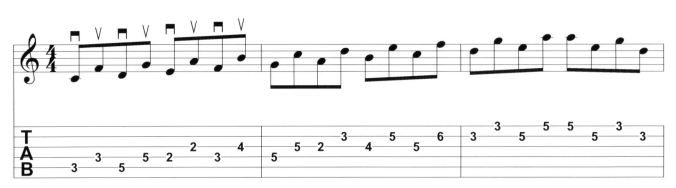

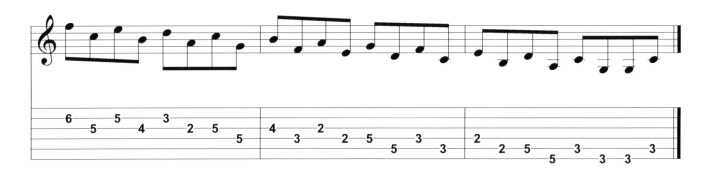

Warm-Up #39

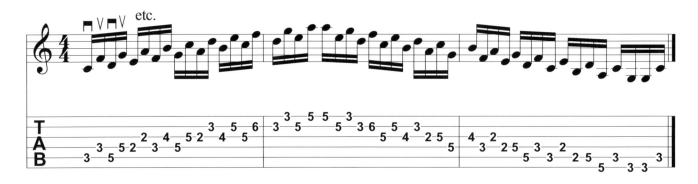

How to Play Warm-Ups #40, #41, and #42

The next three warm-ups move through the C major scale in fifths, starting with the root, skipping the second note, followed by the note five notes away from the root. Then it returns to the note that was skipped. From there it moves up five notes again, and so on.

Warm-Up #40 gives you quarter note rhythms to practice. Number 41 gives you eighth notes to practice, and finally, Warm-Up #42 gives you sixteenth notes to practice.

Again, the fingerings for the following exercises remain the same. (See Chart: How to Play Warm-Up #28.)

Start each warm-up at 60bpm on your metronome and gradually work up to around 120bpm.

Warm-Up #40

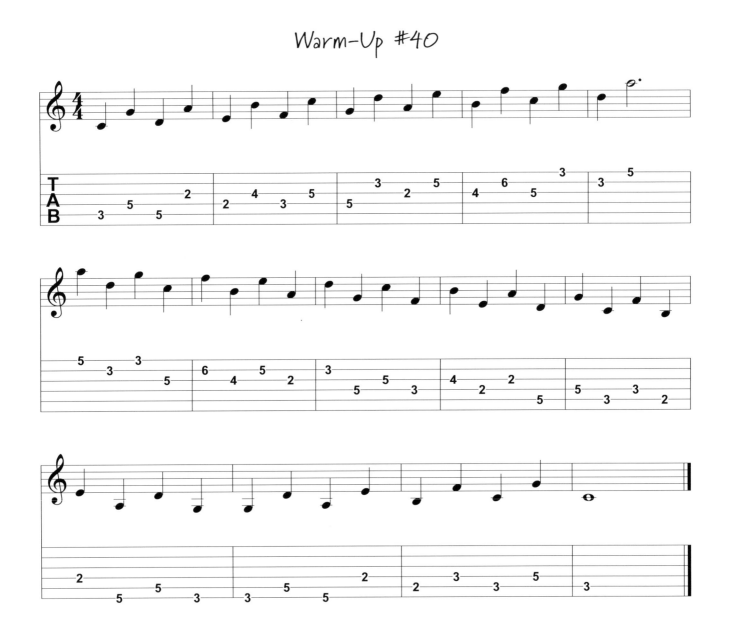

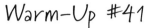

Warm-Up #41

Warm-Up #42

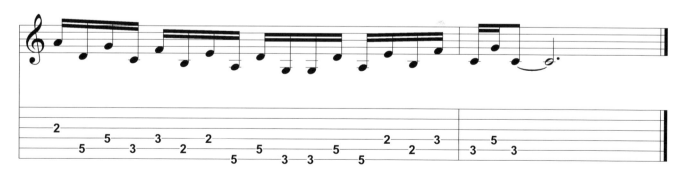

How to Play Warm-Up #43

The following warm-up moves into triplets. However, rather than playing the scale directly in triplets, it moves up three notes and then back one note. Then it then moves up three more, then back, and continues on until all the notes in C major are played. Keep in mind that for each set of triplets the metronome will click one time, so that there are three even notes per beat.

The fingerings for remain the same. (See Chart: How to Play Warm-Up #28.)

Start this warm-up at 60bpm on your metronome and gradually work up to around 120bpm.

Warm-Up #43

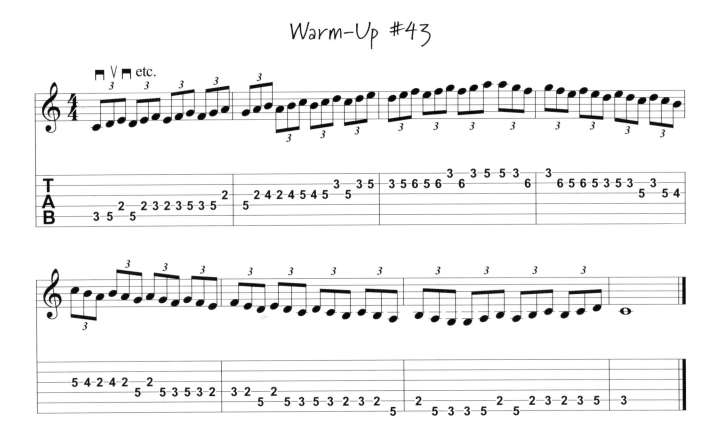

C Major Licks

This section of the unit takes the major scale and shows you how to use the major scale to create licks. That way you can practice the scale in a more musical fashion, rather than simply playing through the scale in a predetermined order.

The fingerings for the following licks remain the same. (See Chart: How to Play Warm-Up #28.)

Begin by setting the metronome at 60bpm and gradually work up to around 120-130bpm for each lick.

Lick #6

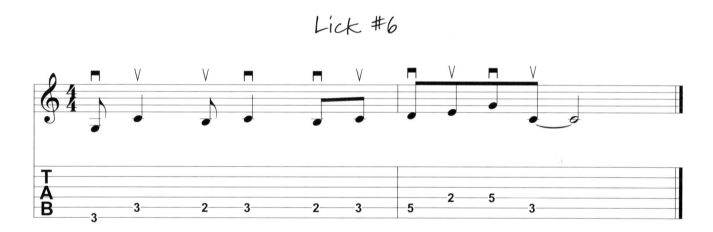

Lick #7

Lick #8

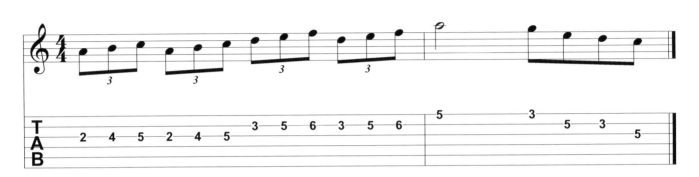

Lick #9

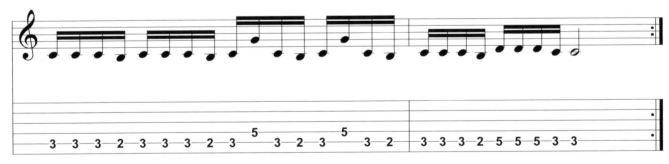

Lick #10

For Lick #10, be sure to swing the eighth notes.

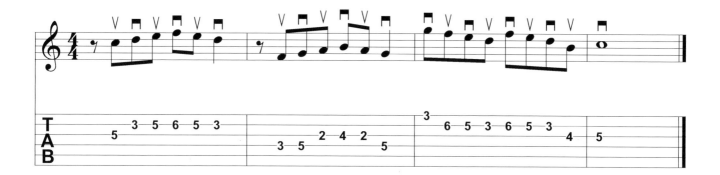

Arpeggio Exercises

The arpeggio exercises in this unit work in the same manner as Unit 2. However, there is one significant change. Instead of immediately descending through each arpeggio, you are going to move through all the ascending arpeggios first, and then practice them all descending.

The fingering for these exercises remains the same as warm-ups found in this unit.

Continue to use your metronome with these exercises. Start off slowly, around 60bpm, and gradually build up speed until you can play these easily around 120bpm. It may take longer to play Arpeggio Exercise #6 up to speed. So take your time with that one.

Arpeggio Exercise #4

Arpeggio Exercise #5

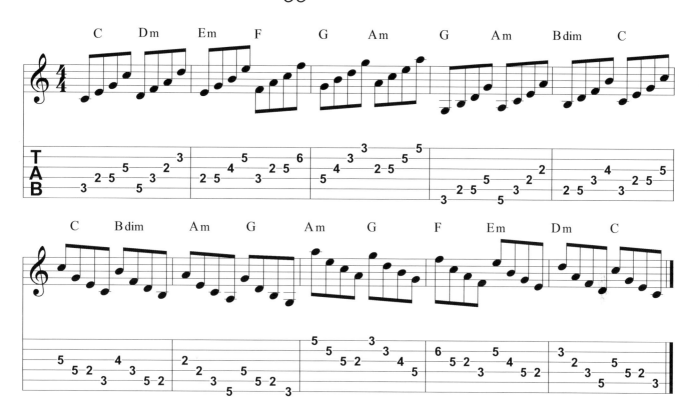

Arpeggio Exercise #6

Unit 4

Pattern 3

Unit 4: Pattern 3 Moving Up the Neck

Use the following chart to play the C major scale with the warm-ups found in this unit. The gray circles show you where the note "C" is found. The black dots indicate scale tones. Start with the lowest string (bottom of the chart) and play each dot in turn, starting with the sixth string, fifth fret, then moving on to seventh fret, then the eighth fret, and so on.

Since this pattern starts on the fifth fret of the last string, the fingering once again changes from the last unit. The first note in the pattern (the "A" note) is played with the index finger. Then it takes the one-finger-per-fret approach for strings 6, 5, and 4. When you get to string 3, you have to shift back one fret, using your first finger for the fourth fret, your second finger for the root note "C" on the fifth fret, and your pinky finger for the note "D" on the seventh fret. When moving to the second string, you'll want to shift back, so that your first finger plays the fifth fret once again. (See chart on the next page.)

When descending through the scale, you'll simply use the same fingerings, but in reverse.

To play this pattern from the root, simply start with the pinky finger on string six, fret eight.

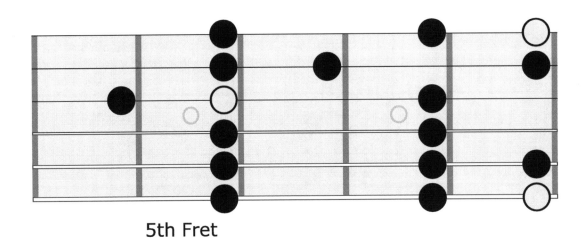

5th Fret

How to Play Warm-Up #44

In this unit, the scale is moved up into the fifth position. (Positions are usually marked by where your first finger is playing. So technically, this pattern slips back to fourth position for the third string.) For Warm-Up #44, you will play through the C major scale starting on the lowest "C" in the pattern, and then play to the next "C" found on third string, completing one octave.

Start the warm-up at 60bpm and work your way up in increments of 5 to 10 until you can play it comfortably at 130bpm. Try to push yourself further once 130bpm feels too easy.

The fingerings for strings 1, 2, 4, 5, and 6:

- Fret 5: Use the index finger (Finger 1)
- Fret 6: Use the middle finger (Finger 2)
- Fret 7: Use the ring finger (Finger 3)
- Fret 8: Use the pinky finger (Finger 4)

For string 3:

- Fret 4: Use the index finger (Finger 1)
- Fret 5: Use the middle finger (Finger 2)
- Fret 7: Use the pinky finger (Finger 4)

Warm-Up #44

How to Play Warm-Ups #45 and #46

The next two warm-ups move through the basic C major scale using eighth notes and then sixteenth notes, respectively.

The fingerings for the following exercises remain the same. (See Chart: How to Play Warm-Up #44.)

Start each warm-up at 60bpm and gradually work up to around 120-130bpm.

Warm-Up #45

60

Warm-Up #46

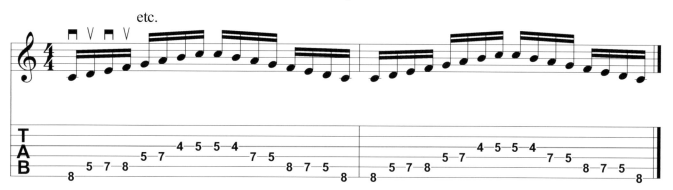

How to Play Warm-Ups #47, #48, and #49

Since there are two full octaves available in this position, you will now practice the second octave in the next three warm-ups. As before, Warm-up #47 uses quarter notes, #48 uses eighth notes, and #49 uses sixteenth notes.

The fingerings for the following exercises are different. Start with the index finger (finger 1) on the fifth fret of the third string. Then use the ring finger for the seventh fret of the third string. After that, the fingering returns to normal for this position.

Start each warm-up at 60bpm and gradually work up to around 120-130bpm.

Warm-Up #47

Warm-Up #48

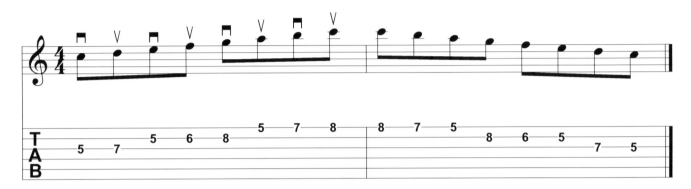

Warm-Up #49

How to Play Warm-Ups #50, #51, #52

For the remainder of this unit, we will be using all the diatonic notes found in this region of the neck. Starting with the lowest root "C", we will travel through two octaves, return to the lowest "C", move down two notes lower, and then return to "C", completing the full box pattern.

Warm-up #50 uses quarter notes, #51 uses eighth notes, and #52 uses sixteenth notes.

Use the fingerings found under the description for Warm-up #44.

Start each warm-up at 60bpm and gradually work up to around 120-130bpm.

Warm-Up #50

Warm-Up #51

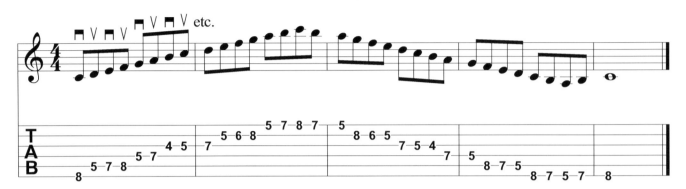

Warm-Up #52

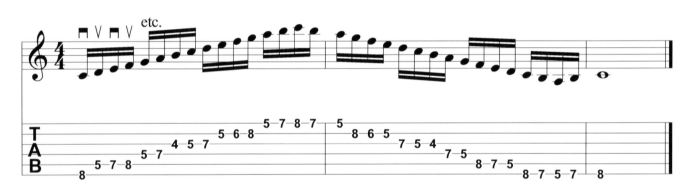

How to Play Warm-Ups #53, #54, #55

The next three warm-ups move through the C major scale in thirds, starting with the root, skipping the second note, playing the third note, then returning to the note that was skipped. From there it moves up a third again, and so on.

Again, the fingerings for the following exercises remain the same. (See Chart: How to Play Warm-Up #44.)

Start each warm-up at 60bpm and gradually work up to around 120-130bpm.

Warm-Up #53

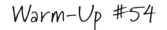

Warm-Up #54

Warm-Up #55

How to Play Warm-Ups #56, #57, #58

The next three warm-ups move through the C major scale in fourths, starting with the root, skipping the second note, playing the fourth note of the scale, then returning to the note that was skipped. From there it moves up a fourth again, and so on.

The fingerings remain the same. (See Chart: How to Play Warm-Up #44.)

Start each warm-up at 60bpm and gradually work up to around 120-130bpm.

Warm-Up #56

Warm-Up #57

Warm-Up #58

How to Play Warm-Ups #59, #60, #61

The next set of warm-ups move through the C major scale in fifths, starting with the root, playing the fifth note of the scale, then returning to the second note of the scale. From there it moves up five notes again, and so on.

The fingerings remain the same. (See Chart: How to Play Warm-Up #44.)

Start each warm-up at 60bpm and gradually work up to around 120-130bpm.

Warm-Up #59

69

Warm-Up #60

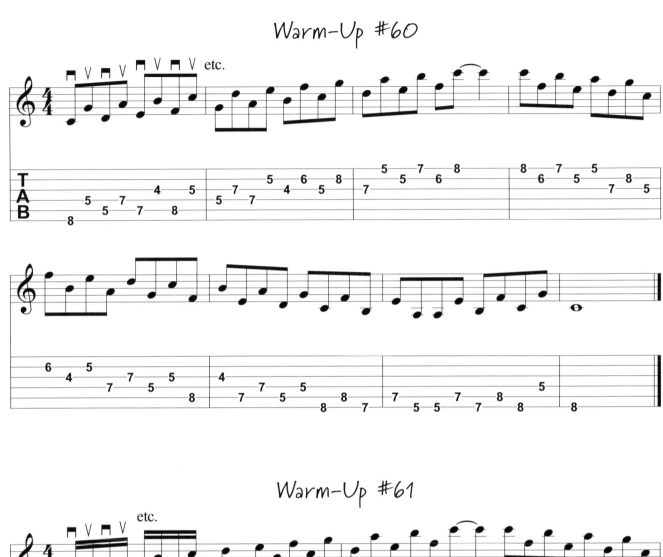

Warm-Up #61

How to Play Warm-Up #62

The following warm-up makes use of triplets. However, just like the other units, rather than playing the scale directly in triplets, it moves up three notes and then back one note, continuing up through the scale in this manner. Keep in mind that for each set of triplets the metronome will click one time, so that there are three even notes per beat.

The fingerings for these warm-ups remain the same. (See Chart: How to Play Warm-Up #44.)

Start each warm-up at 60bpm on your metronome and gradually work up to around 120bpm.

Warm-Up #62

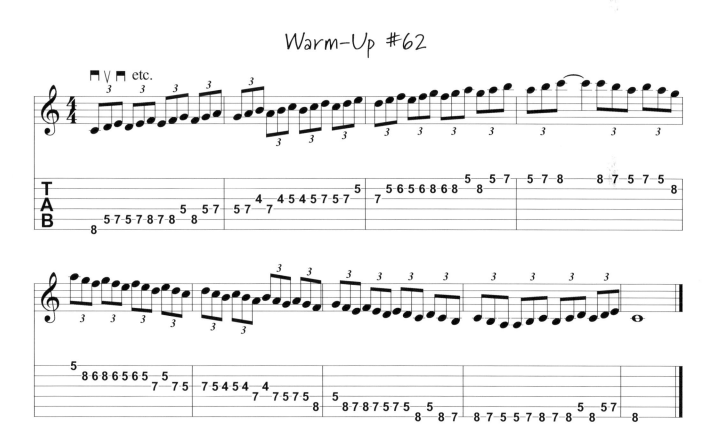

71

Arpeggio Exercises

Practice the following arpeggios. Chord symbols have been included so that you can relate the notes from each chord to their arpeggio.

Use Warm-up #44 fingerings.

Start each warm-up at 60bpm on your metronome and gradually work up to around 120bpm.

Arpeggio Exercise #7

(Arpeggio Exercise #7 Continues on the next page)

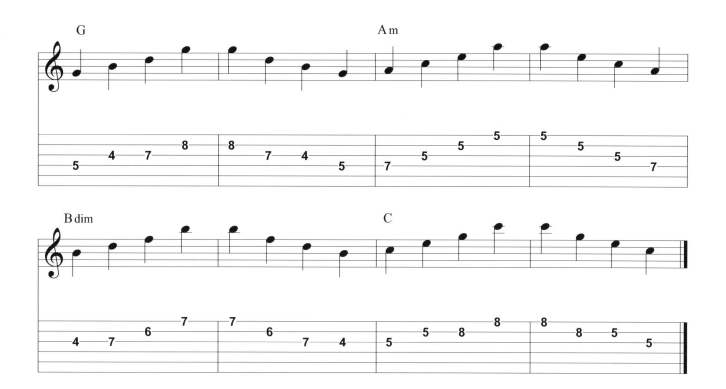

Arpeggio Exercise #8

73

Arpeggio Exercise #9

Major Scale Licks

The following licks are based on the notes studied in this unit. That way you can practice the scale in a more musical fashion, rather than simply playing through the scale in a predetermined order.

The fingerings for the following licks remain the same. (See Chart: How to Play Warm-Up #44.)

Begin by setting the metronome at 60bpm and gradually work up to around 120-130bpm for each lick.

Lick #11

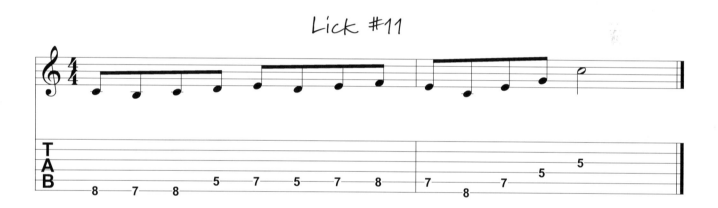

Lick #12

Lick #13

Lick #14

Lick #15

Connecting Patterns

The following examples combine patterns 1 (from Unit 2) and 2 (from Unit 3) , 2 and 3 (from Unit 4), and then all three together to show you how to connect the different patterns together to expand the range of notes available to you. These are not the only ways of moving between patterns, but it will help show you how to get started doing so.

Start each one at 60bpm on your metronome and gradually work up to around 120bpm.

Connecting Patterns 1 and 2

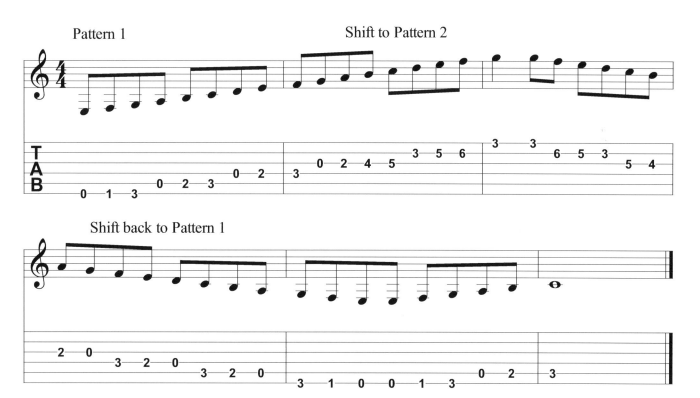

Connecting Patterns 2 and 3

Connecting Patterns 1, 2, and 3

Unit 5

Pattern 4

Use the following chart to play the C major scale with the warm-ups found in this unit. The gray circles show you where the note "C" is found. The black dots indicate scale tones. Start with the lowest string (bottom of the chart) and play each dot in turn, starting with the sixth string, eighth fret, then moving on to the tenth fret, and so on.

Start with your middle finger, not your index. Then use the pinky finger to get the "D" on the tenth fret. When you move to the fifth string, start with the index finger on the seventh fret, the middle finger on the eighth fret, and then the pinky on fret ten.

Note that on the first string, the note "C" (eighth fret) can be the last note you play before moving back down the strings. When doing so, you'll have played a full two octaves. The additional "D" on the first string (tenth fret) is optional.

When descending through the scale, use the same fingerings but in reverse.

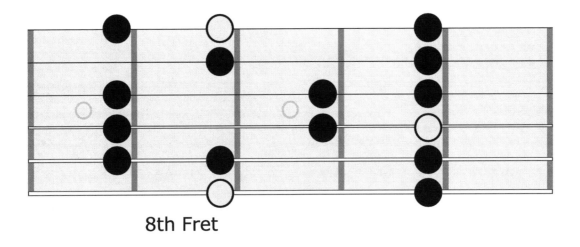

8th Fret

How to Play Warm-Ups #63, #64, and #65

In this unit, the scale is moved up to the seventh position. For Warm-Up #63, you will play through the C major scale using quarter notes, starting on the lowest "C" in the pattern, which happens to be the lowest note of the pattern, and then playing to the next "C" found on fourth string, completing one octave.

Warm-up #64 does the same using eighth notes, and Warm-up #65 uses sixteenth notes.

The fingerings for this unit:

- Fret 7: Use the index finger (Finger 1)

- Fret 8: Use the middle finger (Finger 2)

- Fret 9: Use the ring finger (Finger 3)

- Fret 10: Use the pinky finger (Finger 4)

As before, start the warm-up at 60bpm and work your way up in increments of 5 to 10 until you can play it comfortably at 130bpm. Try to push yourself further once 130bpm feels too easy.

Warm-Up #63

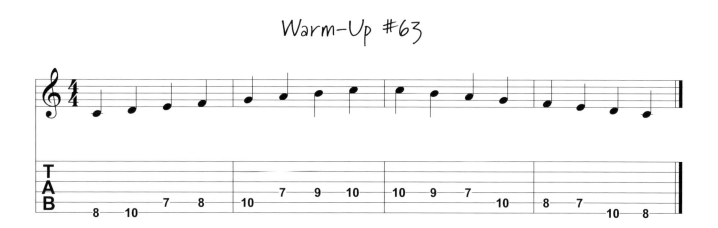

Warm-Up #64

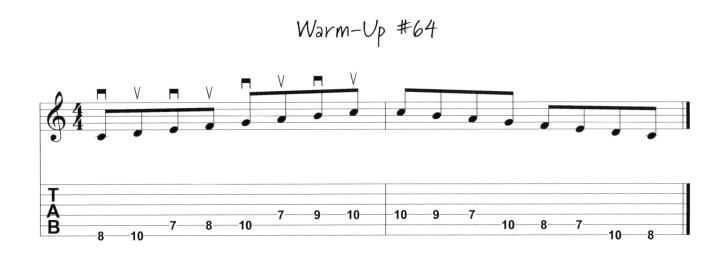

Warm-Up #65

How to Play Warm-Ups #66, #67, and #68

The next three warm-ups are played in a similar manner to the previous three. However, this time, we will be playing them up an octave. Continue using the same fingerings and metronome settings.

Warm-Up #66

Warm-Up #67

Warm-Up #68

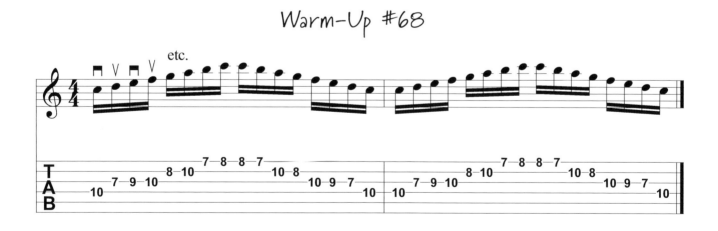

How to Play Warm-Ups #69, #70, and #71

For the remainder of this unit, we will be using all the diatonic notes found in this region of the neck. Starting with the lowest root "C", we will travel through two octaves before returning to the lowest "C". Essentially, we will be connecting the two previous sets of warm-ups into one complete two-octave warm-up.

Use the fingerings found under the description for Warm-up #63.

Start each warm-up at 60bpm and gradually work up to around 120-130bpm.

Warm-Up #69

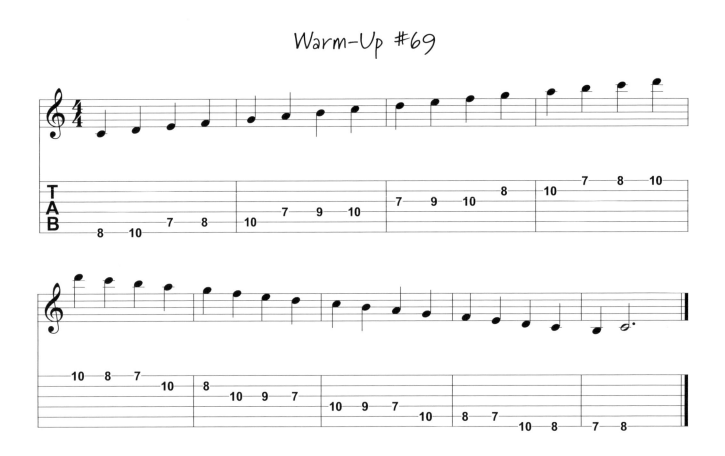

Warm-Up #70

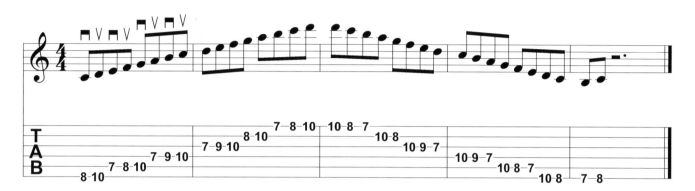

Warm-Up #71

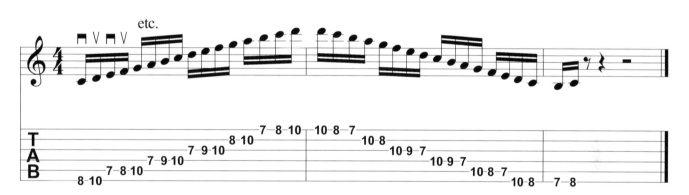

How to Play Warm-Ups #72, #73, and #74

In the next three exercises you will continue to practice the C Major scale in pattern 4, but this time in thirds, just like we have in past units.

Use the fingerings found under the description for Warm-up #63.

Start each warm-up at 60bpm and gradually work up to around 120-130bpm.

Warm-Up #72

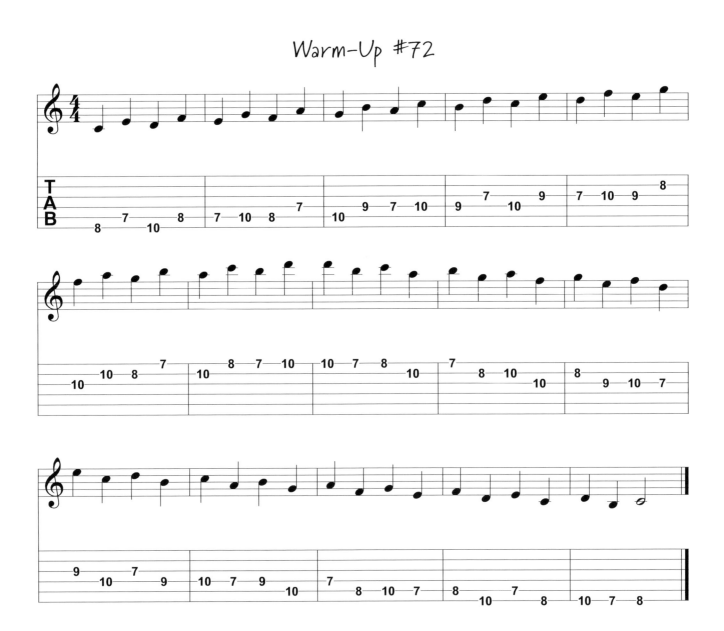

Warm-Up #73

Warm-Up #74

87

How to Play Warm-Ups #75, #76, and #77

In the next three exercises you will continue to practice the C Major scale in pattern 4, but now in fourths.

Use the fingerings found under the description for Warm-up #63.

Start each warm-up at 60bpm and gradually work up to around 120-130bpm.

Warm-Up #75

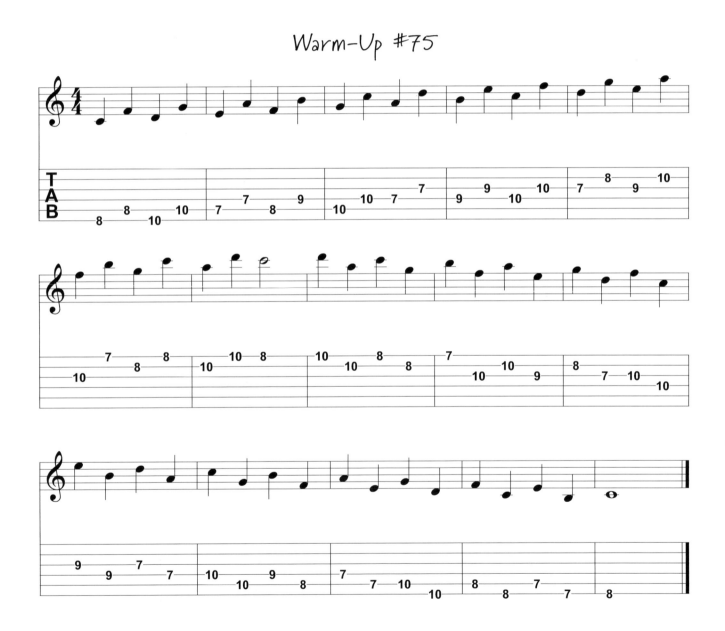

88

Warm-Up #76

Warm-Up #77

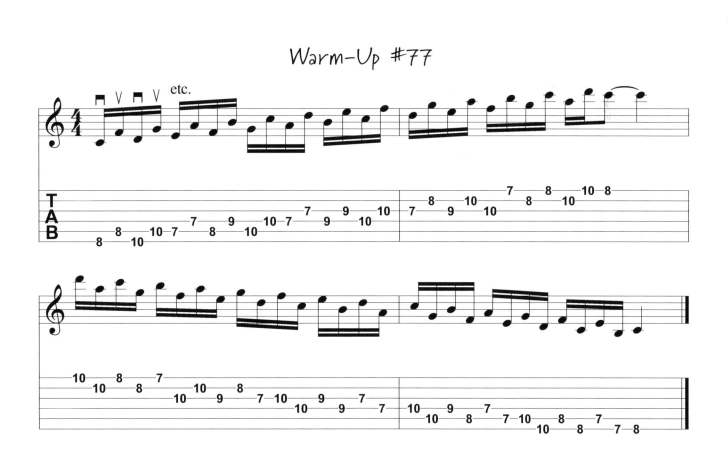

How to Play Warm-Ups #78, #79, and #80

For the next three warm-ups, you will now play the major scale in fifths. Use the fingerings found under the description for Warm-up #63.

Start each warm-up at 60bpm and gradually work up in increments of 5 to 10 until you can play it around 120-130bpm.

Warm-Up #78

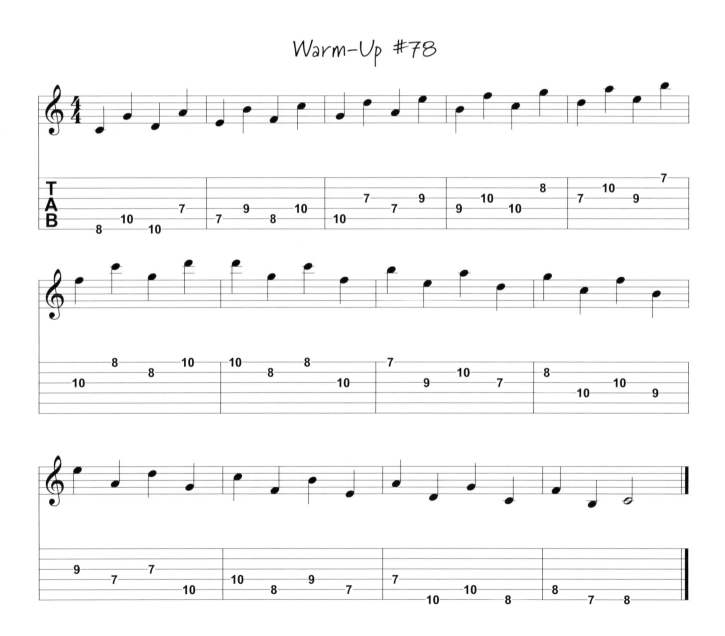

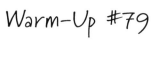

Warm-Up #79

Warm-Up #80

How to Play Warm-Up #81

The following warm-up makes use of triplets, moving up three notes and then back one note, continuing up through the scale in this manner. Keep in mind that for each set of triplets the metronome will click one time, so that there are three even notes per beat.

Use the fingerings found under the description for Warm-up #63.

Begin this warm-up at 60bpm and gradually work up in increments of 5 to 10 until you can play it around 120bpm.

Warm-Up #81

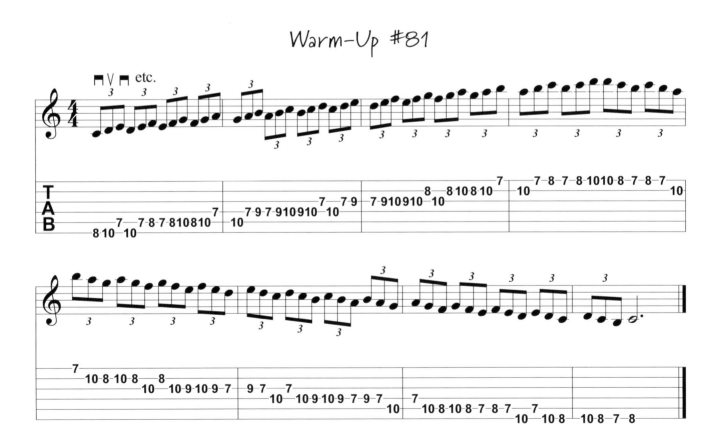

Arpeggio Exercises

Practice the following arpeggio exercises. Chord symbols have been included so that you can relate the notes from each chord to their arpeggio.

Use Warm-up #63 fingerings.

Start each warm-up at 60bpm on your metronome and gradually work up to around 120bpm.

Arpeggio Exercise #10

Arpeggio Exercise #10 (continued)

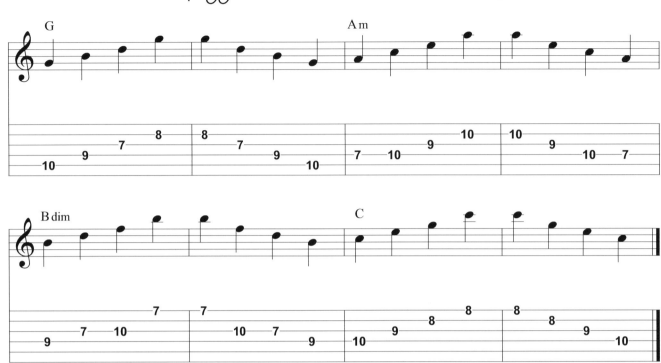

Arpeggio Exercise #11

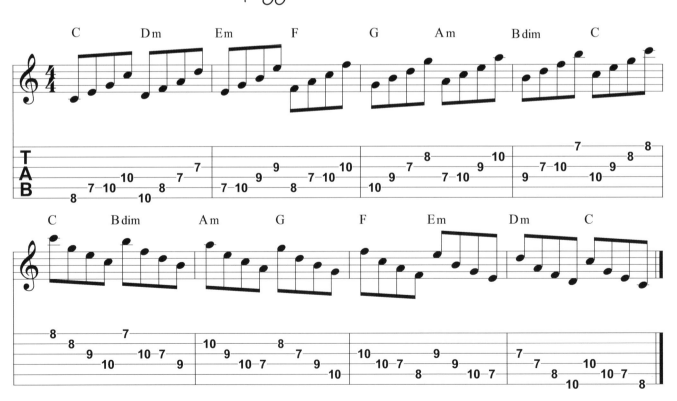

Arpeggio Exercise #12

Major Scale Licks

The following licks are based on the notes studied in this unit. That way you can practice the scale in a more musical fashion, rather than simply playing through the scale in a predetermined order.

The fingerings for the following licks remain the same. (See Chart: How to Play Warm-Up #63.)

Begin by setting the metronome at 60bpm and gradually work up to around 120-130bpm for each lick.

Lick #16

Lick #17

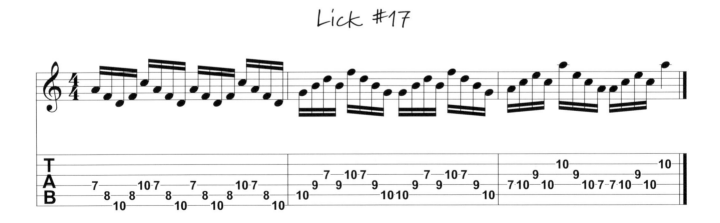

Lick #18

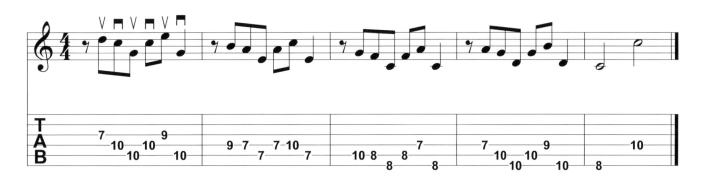

Lick #19

Lick #20

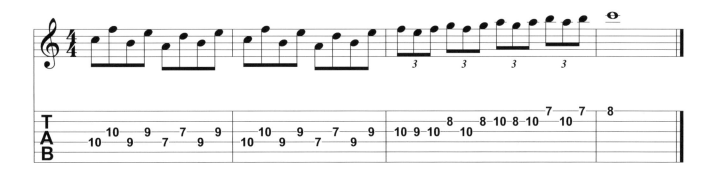

Connecting Patterns

The following examples combine patterns 3 and 4; 2, 3, and 4; and then all of them together to show you how to connect the different patterns to expand the range of notes available to you. These are not the only ways of moving among patterns, but it will help show you how to get started doing so.

Start each one at 60bpm on your metronome and gradually work up to around 120bpm.

Connecting Patterns 3 and 4

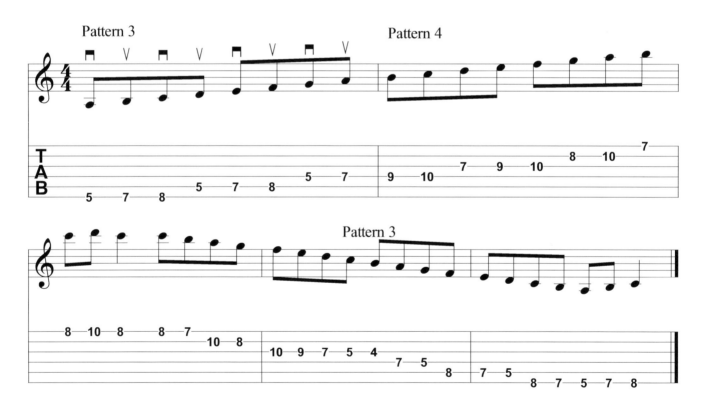

Connecting Patterns 2, 3, and 4

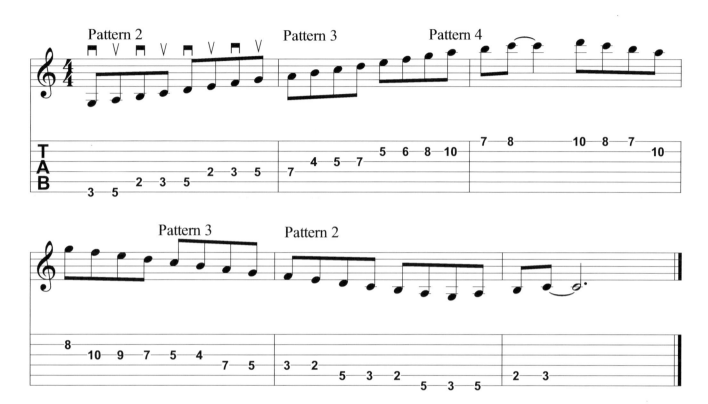

Connecting Patterns 1-4

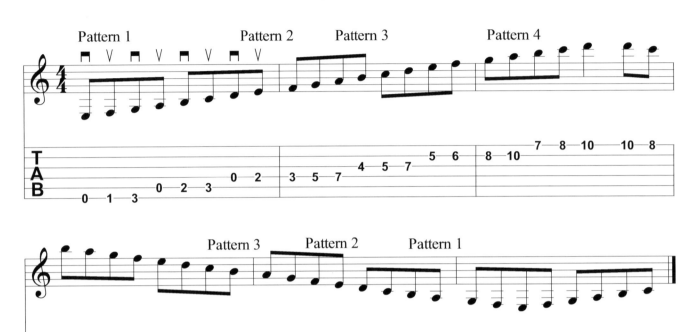

Unit 6

Pattern 5

Use the following chart to play the C major scale with the warm-ups found in this unit. The gray circles show you where the note "C" is found. The black dots indicate scale tones. Start with the lowest string (bottom of the chart) and play each dot in turn, starting with the sixth string, tenth fret, then moving on to the twelfth fret, up to the thirteenth, then on to the notes on the next string.

Start with the index finger on the note "D", last string, 10th fret. Then use the third finger for the 12th fret and the pinky for the 13th. When moving to the fourth string, you'll need to shift back a fret and use your index finger on the 9th fret. When you move to the second string, shift back so that your index finger is playing the 10th fret once again. (See chart on the next page.)

To play a single one-octave major scale, start on the note "C", fourth string, 10th fret with the middle finger and play up to the second string, 13th fret.

When descending through the scale, use the same fingerings but in reverse order.

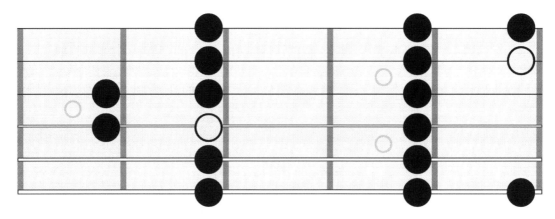

9th Fret

How to Play Warm-Ups #82, 83, and 84

In this unit, the scale has moved up to the 9th position. For Warm-Up #82, you will play through the C major scale using quarter notes, starting on the lowest "C" in the pattern and then playing up to the next "C", completing one octave.

As in past units, warm-up #83 does the same using eighth notes, and Warm-up #84 uses sixteenth notes.

As before, start the warm-up at 60bpm and work your way up in increments of 5 to 10 until you can play it comfortably at 130bpm. Try to push yourself further once 130bpm feels too easy.

Fingerings for this Unit:

Fret	String 6	String 5	String 4	String 3	String 2	String 1
9	--	--	Index/ Finger 1	Index/ Finger 1	--	--
10	Index/ Finger 1	Index/ Finger 1	Middle/ Finger 2	Middle/ Finger 2	Index/ Finger 1	Index/ Finger 1
11	--	--	--	--	--	--
12	Ring/ Finger 3	Ring/ Finger 3	Pinky/ Finger 4	Pinky/ Finger 4	Ring/ Finger 3	Ring/ Finger 3
13	Pinky/ Finger 4	Pinky/ Finger 4	--	--	Pinky/ Finger 4	Pinky/ Finger 4

Warm-Up #82

Warm-Up #83

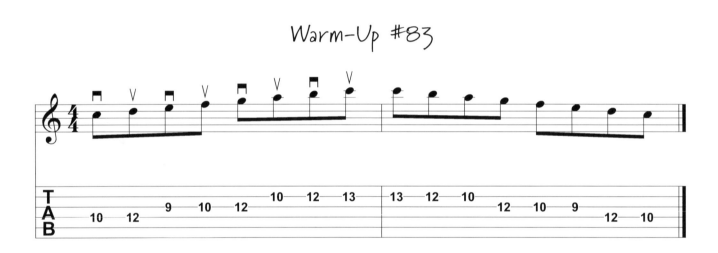

Warm-Up #84

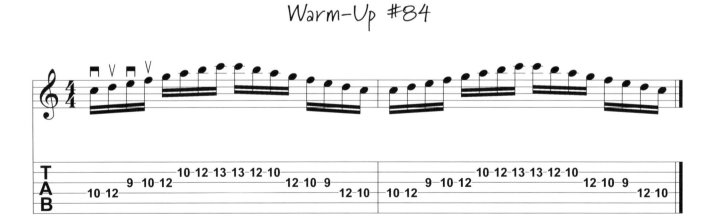

How to Play Warm-Ups #85, #86, and #87

For the rest of this unit, we will be using all the diatonic notes found in this region of the neck. Starting with the lowest root "C", we will travel through the octave, moving beyond it into a partial second octave before returning to the lowest "C". From there we will move down to the lowest note available in this region of the neck before making our way back to the root C on the fourth string, tenth fret. Use the fingerings found under the description for Warm-up #82.

Start each warm-up at 60bpm and gradually work up to around 120-130bpm.

Warm-Up #85

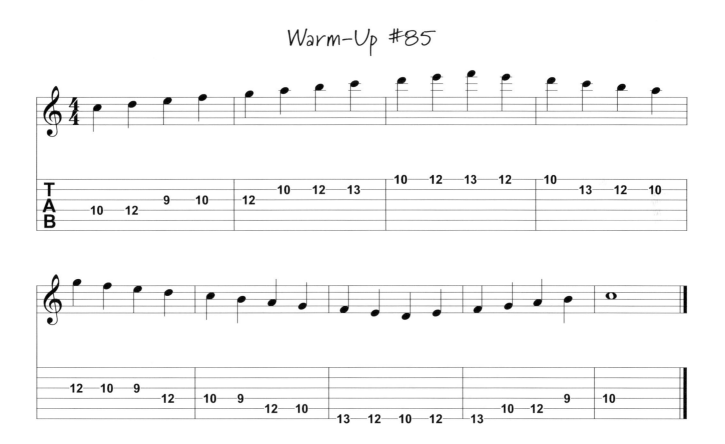

Warm-Up #86

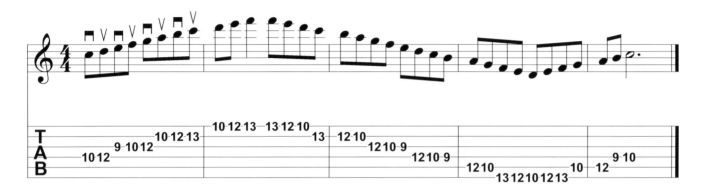

Warm-Up #87

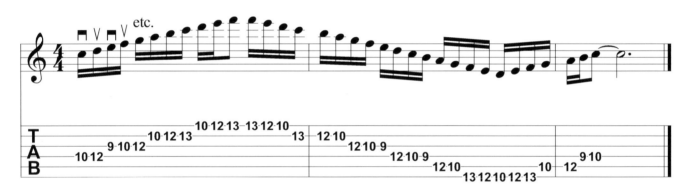

How to Play Warm-Ups #88, #89, and #90

In the next three exercises you will continue to practice the C Major scale pattern 5, but this time in thirds, just like we have in past units.

Use the fingerings found under the description for Warm-up #82.

Start each warm-up at 60bpm and gradually work up to around 120-130bpm.

Warm-Up #88

Warm-Up #89

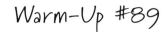

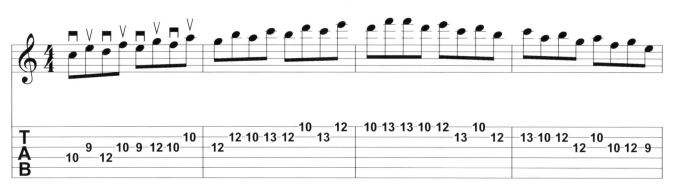

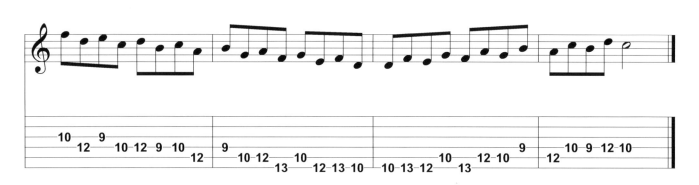

Warm-Up #90

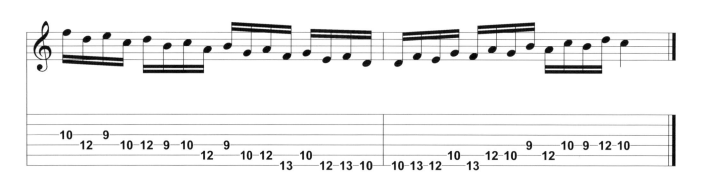

108

How to Play Warm-Ups #91, #92, and #93

In the next three exercises you will continue to practice the C Major scale in pattern 5, but now in fourths, just like we have in past units.

Use the fingerings found under the description for Warm-up #82. However, you may find it necessary to change some of the fingerings in these exercises to make them easier to play, especially at faster tempos.

For example, in Warm-up #91 the first two notes are both on the tenth fret of adjacent strings. Therefore, it is easier and more efficient to use the index finger on the first on and then the middle finger on the second one. Then when moving up to the two notes on the 12th fret, you may want to start with the second finger on string four and then use the third finger on string three. This is just one possible re-fingering; you may discover for yourself something that works for you. Always aim for efficiency, clarity, and ease of playing.

Start each warm-up at 60bpm and gradually work up to around 120-130bpm.

Warm-Up #91

Warm-Up #92

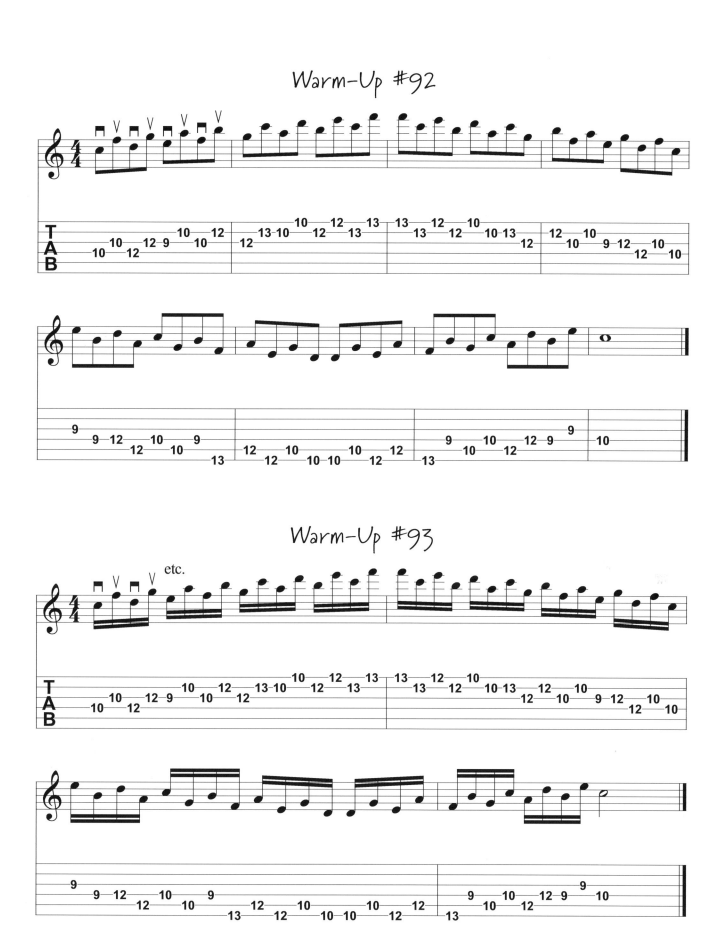

Warm-Up #93

111

How to Play Warm-Ups #94, #95, and #96

In the next three exercises you will continue to practice the C Major scale in pattern 5, but now in fifths.

Use the fingerings found under the description for Warm-up #82. However, you may find it necessary to change some of the fingerings in this exercise as well in order to make it easier to play, especially at faster tempos.

Start each warm-up at 60bpm and gradually work up to around 120-130bpm.

Warm-Up #94

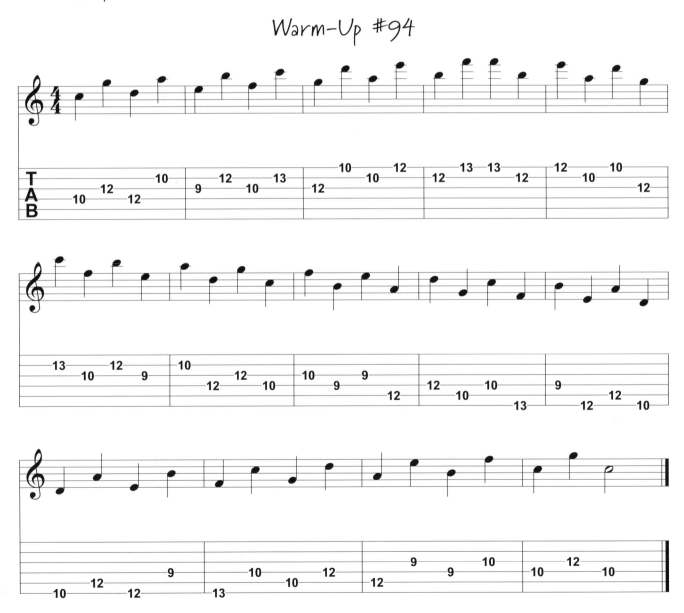

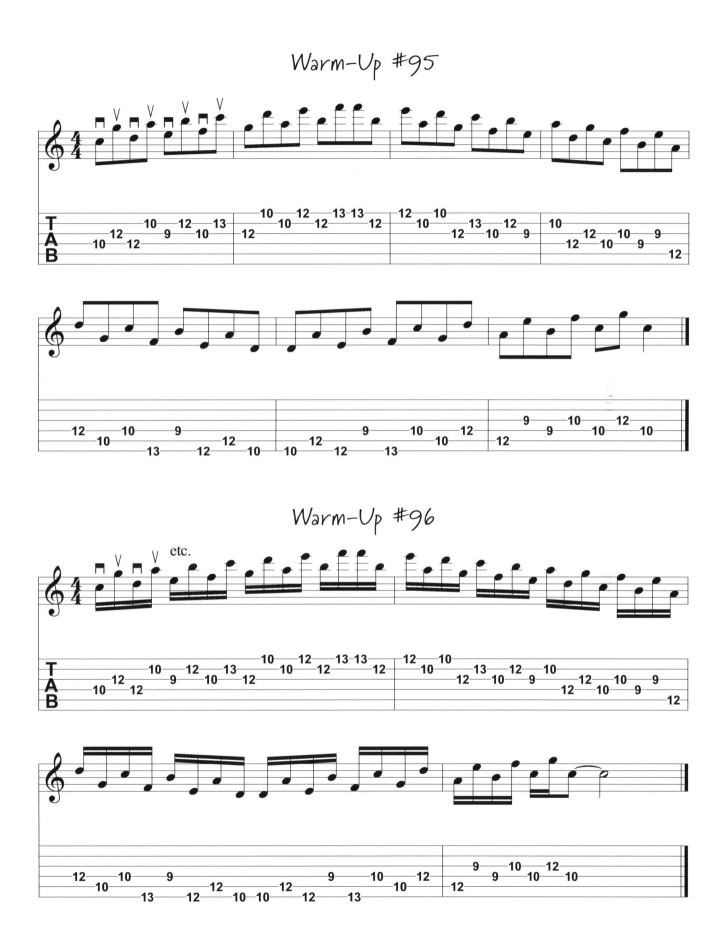

How to Play Warm-Up #97

The following warm-up uses triplets, moving up three notes and then back one note, continuing through the scale in this manner.

Use the fingerings found under the description for Warm-up #82.

Start each warm-up at 60bpm and gradually work up in increments of 5 to 10 until you can play it around 120bpm.

Warm-Up #97

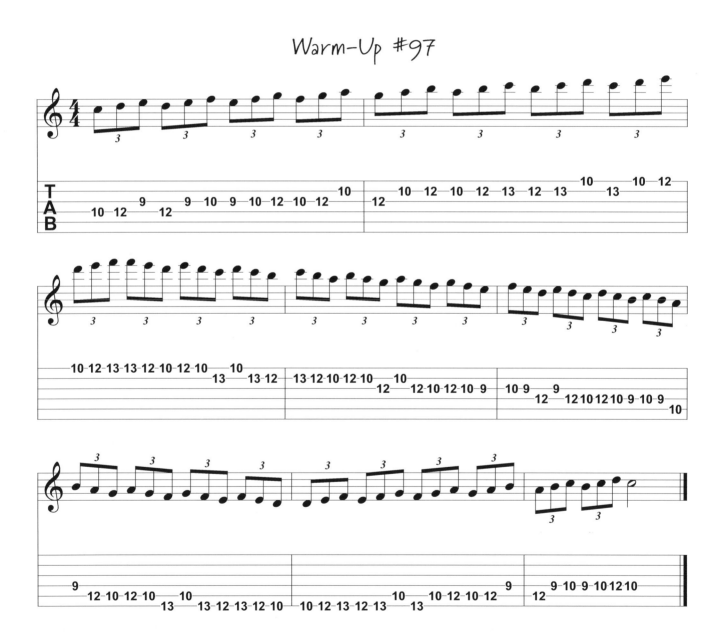

Arpeggio Exercises

Practice the following arpeggio exercises. Chord symbols have been included so that you can relate the notes from each chord to their arpeggio. Arpeggio exercises 13 and 14 include two octaves of some of the arpeggios where possible. However, for the sake of simplicity, Arpeggio exercise 15 does not include the additional octaves.

Use Warm-up #82 fingerings.

Start each warm-up at 60bpm on your metronome and gradually work up to around 120bpm.

Arpeggio Exercise #13

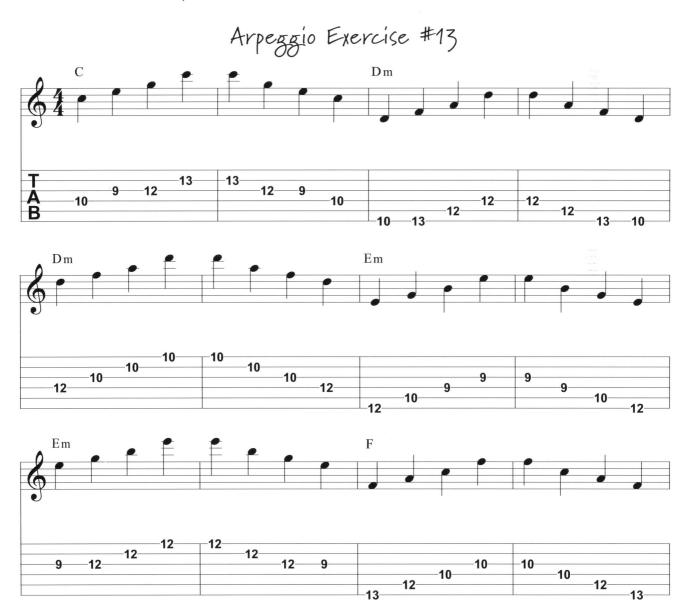

115

Arpeggio Exercise #13 (continued)

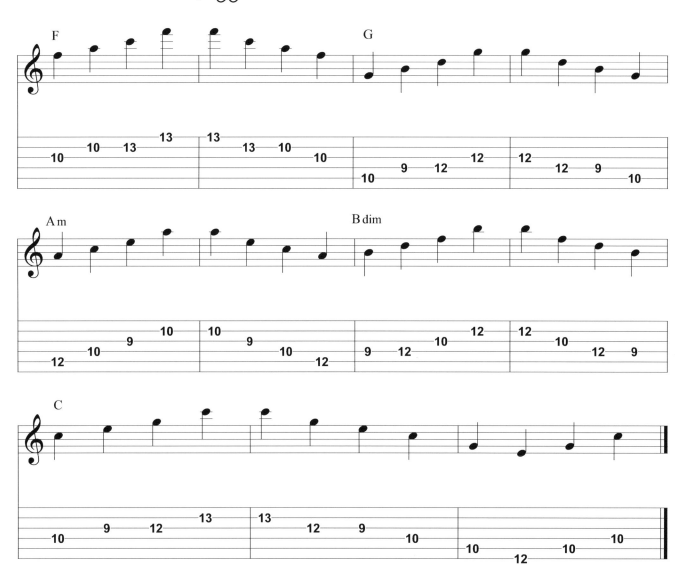

Arpeggio Exercise #14

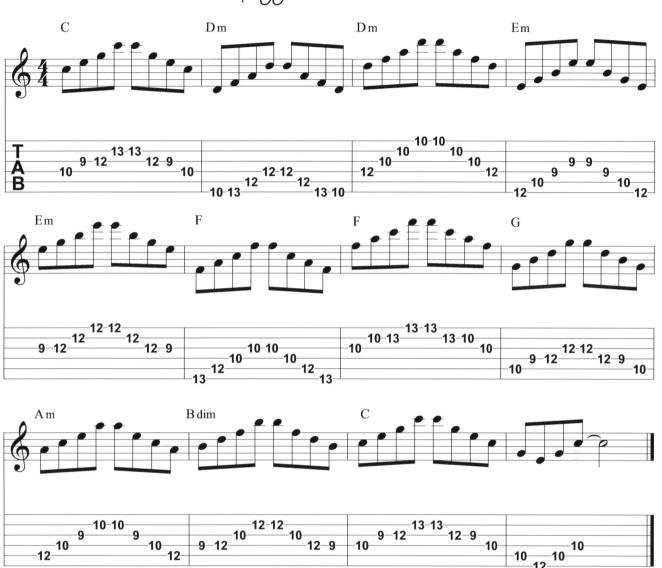

Arpeggio Exercise #15

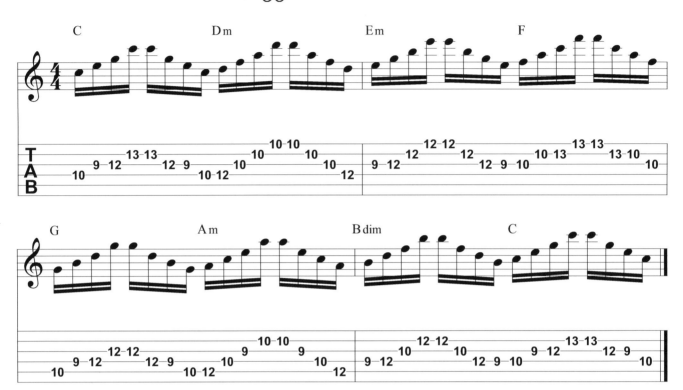

Major Scale Licks

The following licks are based on the notes studied in this unit. That way you can practice the scale in a more musical fashion rather than simply playing through the scale in a predetermined order.

The fingerings for the following licks remain the same. (See Chart: How to Play Warm-Up #82.)

Begin by setting the metronome at 60bpm and gradually work up to around 120bpm for each lick.

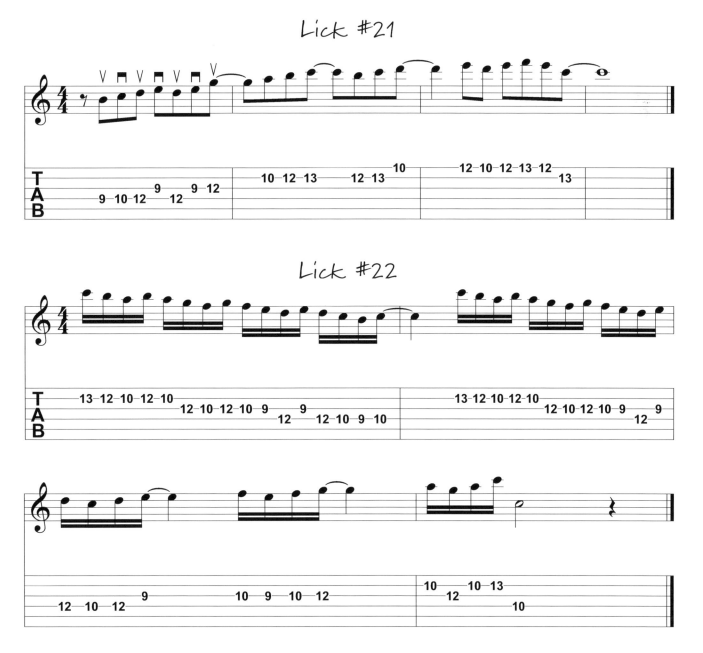

Lick #23

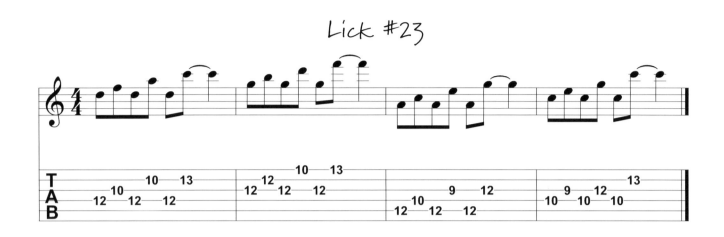

Lick #24

Lick #25

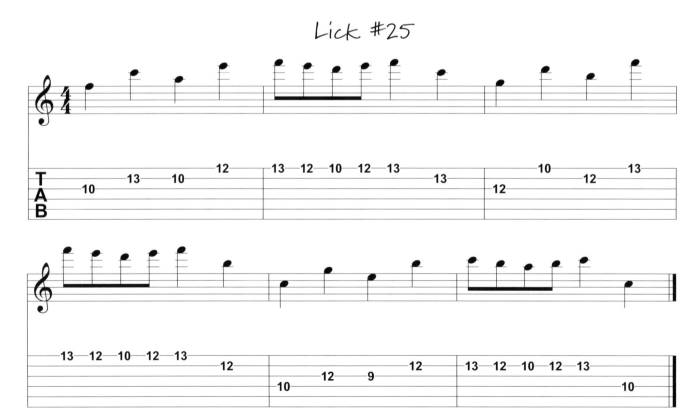

Connecting Patterns

The following examples combines patterns 4 and 5; 3, 4, and 5; 2, 3, 4, and 5; and then all of them together to show you how to connect the different patterns to expand the range of notes available to you. These are not the only ways of moving among the patterns, but it will help show you how to get started doing so.

Start each one at 60bpm on your metronome and gradually work up to around 120bpm.

Connecting Patterns 4 and 5

In this exercise, be sure to start with the middle finger (finger 2) while playing through the C major scale using Pattern 4. Then on the last full beat of measure 1, shift up to Pattern 5 using your index finger (finger 1) so that you'll use your index finger on the 7th fret. Then shift it up to the 9th fret. That will set you up to play Pattern 5 without interruption. Do the same when descending.

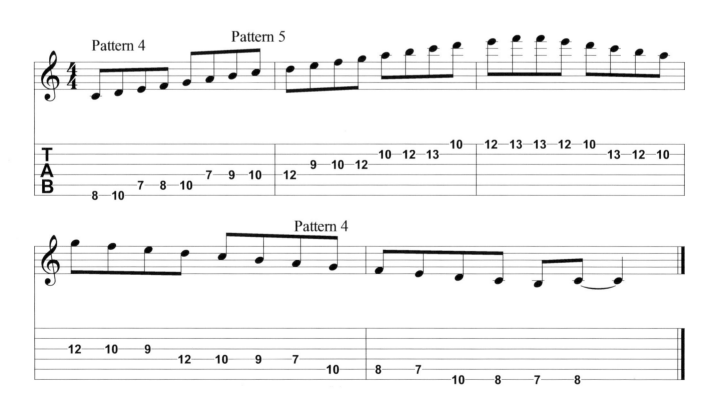

Connecting Patterns 3, 4, and 5

In this exercise, start with the index finger to begin Pattern 3. On string 4 shift to Pattern 4 from frets 5 to 7 using the index finger. Shift again on string 3 from frets 7 to 9 to move into Pattern 5. When descending, shift to Pattern 4 in measure 4, using the index finger to move from the 9th fret to the 7th. Then shift to Pattern 3 in measure 5 using the index finger to move from fret 7 down to 5. Then finish out in Pattern 3.

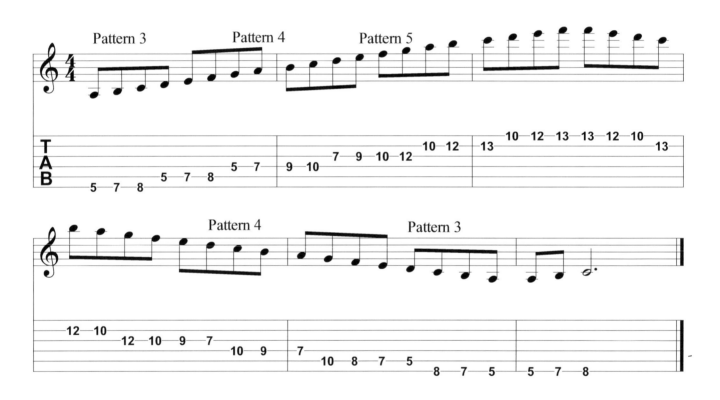

Connecting Patterns 2, 3, 4, and 5

In this exercise, start with the middle finger on the first note. Then at the very end of measure 1, shift to Pattern 3 using the middle finger. Therefore, fret 2 will be played with the index finger, fret 3 with the middle finger, then fret 5 with the middle finger.

For the next shift into Pattern 4, use the fourth finger to play the 7th fret, but then use finger three to get the 9th fret and finger four to get the 10th. Then in that same pattern, shift to the index finger to get the 8th fret on string 2. Then use that same finger to shift up to fret 10 to start playing Pattern 5.

The first shift when descending happens in measure 4. Use the index finger on the 2nd string, 10th fret and then shift that down to the 8th. The next shift in measure 5 is on string 4 moving from the 7th fret to 5th. In this case, use the index finger. On the fifth string, shift from the 5th fret to the third using the second finger. Then play out the exercise in Pattern 2.

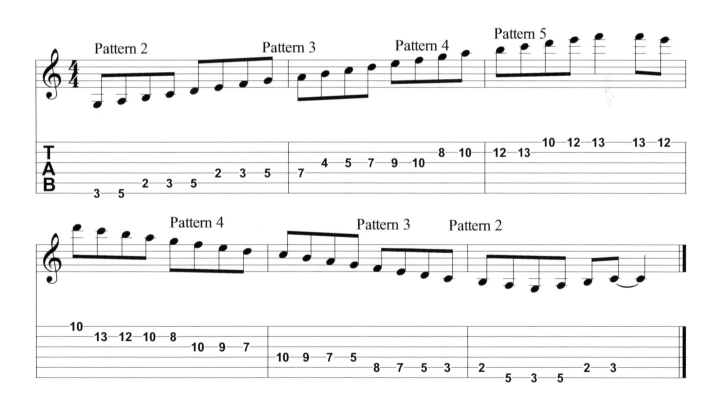

Connecting Patterns 1- 5

In this exercise, the pattern indicators have been intentionally omitted to test your ability to move from one pattern to the next smoothly. Notes from all 5 patterns are represented here. We start with the open last string and move all the way up to the first string's 13th fret! There are many, many ways to approach this. Below is only one of these many approaches. So take your time, watch the tablature carefully, and try to recognize when you are moving from one pattern into the next.

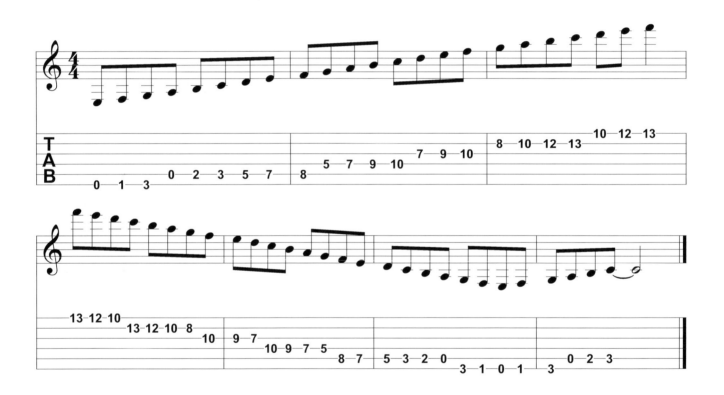

Unit 7

Up an Octave

Unit 7: Pattern 1 Up an Octave

This unit takes the box pattern you learned in Unit 2 and moves it up an octave. Since you've already explored this pattern, each warm-up will only be shown as eighth notes. For further practice, simply take the eighth note exercises and try them as sixteenth notes, triplets, or slow them down to quarter notes as needed.

Use the chart below to play the C major scale with the warm-ups found in this unit. The gray circles show you where the root of the scale "C" is found. The black dots indicate scale tones. Start with the 5th string, 15th fret and play each dot in turn, just as you have in all the past units.

Fingerings for this Unit:

Fret	Finger
12	Index/Finger 1
13	Middle/Finger 2
14	Ring/Finger 3
15	Pinky/Finger 4

As before, start the warm-up at 60bpm and work your way up in increments of 5 to 10 until you can play it comfortably at 130bpm. Try to push yourself further once 130bpm feels too easy.

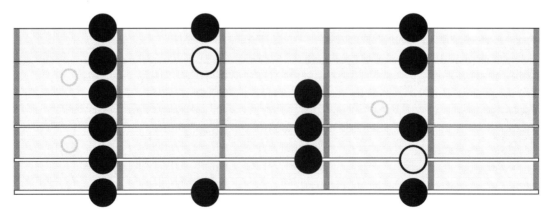

12th Fret

Warm-Up #98

Warm-Up #98 is simply the C major scale from root to its octave. Play it first as eighth notes. Then try the same exercise as sixteenth notes. Be sure to use the metronome.

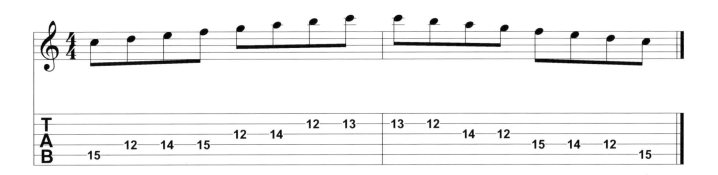

Warm-Up #99

Warm-Up #99 extends to all available notes found in C major in this region of the neck. Starting with the root, moving past the octave, back to the root, down to the low E and then back to the root. Play it first as eighth notes, then try the same exercise as sixteenth notes. Be sure to use the metronome.

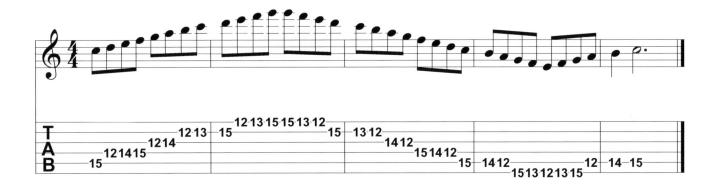

Warm-Up #100

Warm-Up #100 takes you through the full box pattern, but this time in thirds. Play it first as eighth notes, and then try the same exercise as sixteenth notes. Be sure to use the metronome.

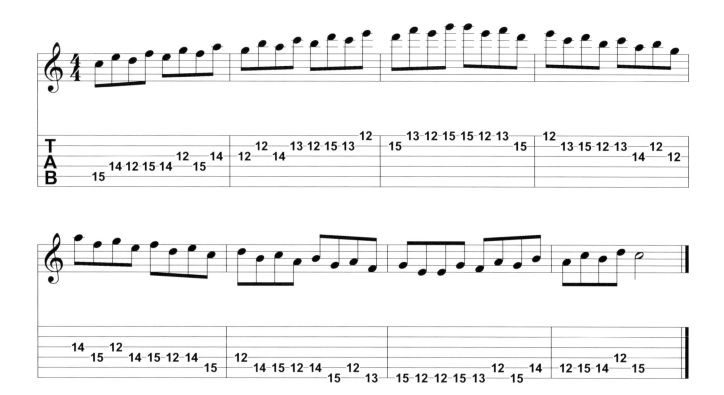

Warm-Up #101

Warm-Up #101 takes you through the full box pattern in fourths. Play it first as eighth notes, and then try the same exercise as sixteenth notes. Be sure to use the metronome.

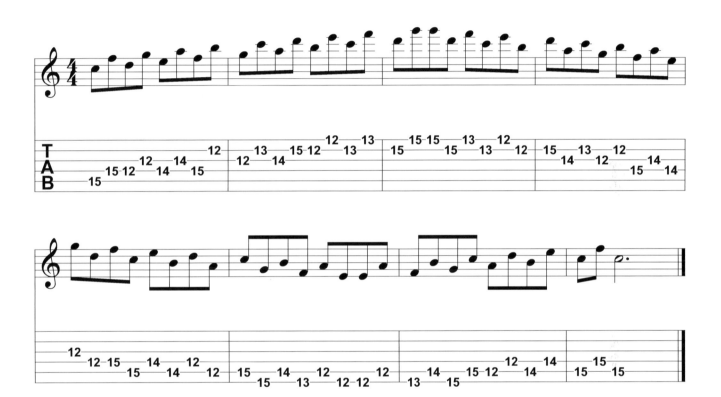

Warm-Up #102

Warm-Up #102 takes you through the full box pattern in fifths. Play it first as eighth notes, and then try the same exercise as sixteenth notes. Be sure to use the metronome.

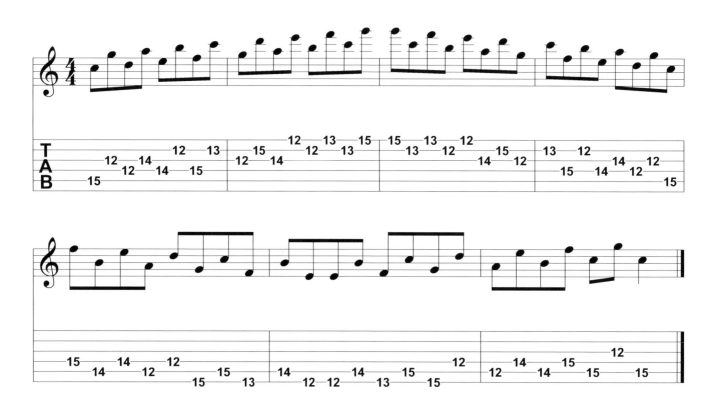

Warm-Up #103

Warm-Up #103 takes you through the C major scale in triplets, but just as before, you will go up three notes, back one, up three, etc. until you've played every diatonic note in this position of the neck.

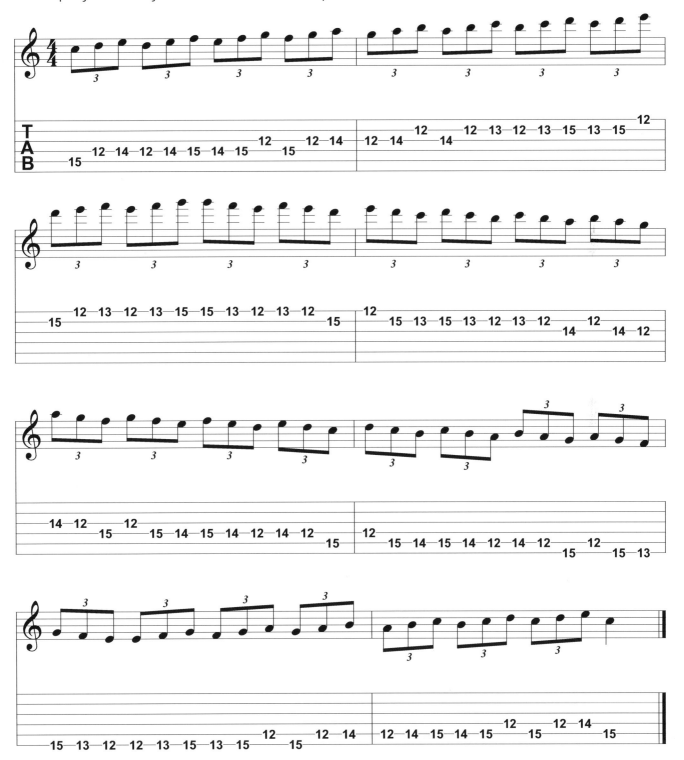

Arpeggio Exercise

Practice the following arpeggio exercise. Chord symbols have been included so you can relate the notes from each chord to their arpeggio. Play it first as eighth notes, then try the same exercise as sixteenth notes.

Start each warm-up at 60bpm on your metronome and gradually work up to around 120bpm.

Arpeggio Exercise #16

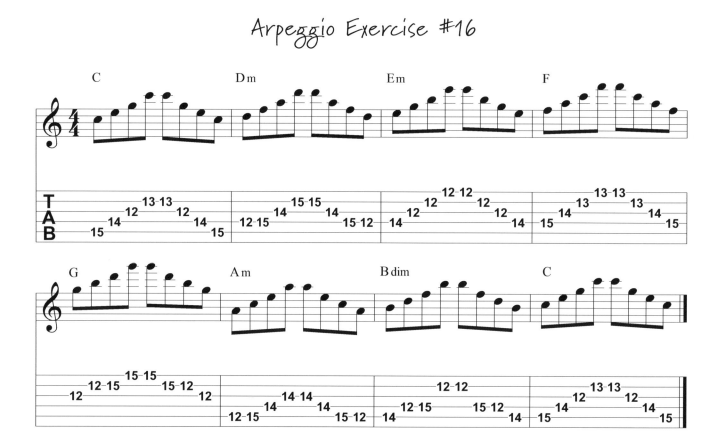

Major Scale Licks

The following licks are based on the notes studied in this unit. That way you can practice the scale in a more musical fashion rather than simply playing through the scale in a predetermined order. These are the same licks found in Unit 2, but this time they are being played an octave higher.

The fingerings for the following licks remain the same as the rest of this unit.

Begin by setting the metronome at 60bpm and gradually work up to around 120-130bpm for each lick.

Lick #26

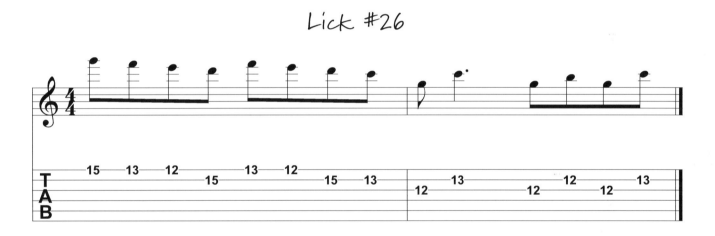

Lick #27

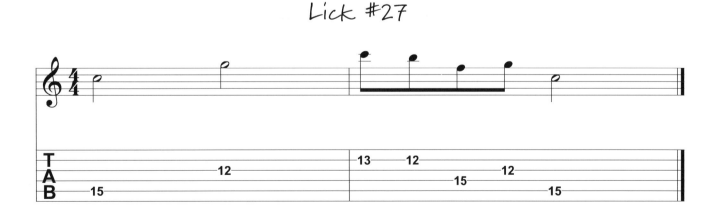

Lick #28

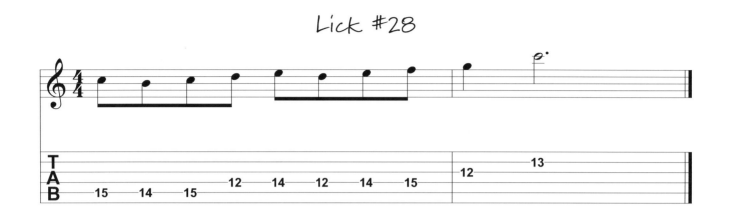

Lick #29

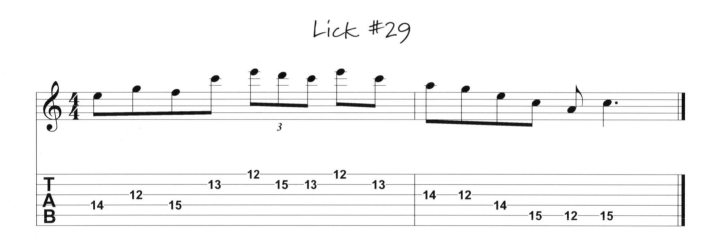

Lick #30

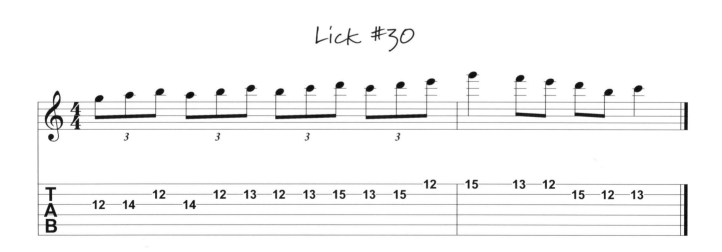

Unit 8

3 Notes Per String

Unit 8: The Three Notes Per String Approach

So far in this book you have learned the major scale using the traditional box-pattern approach. This means you have learned how to play the major scale in six positions with five different finger patterns, from open position all the way to 12th position, covering every possible note in C major.

However, this is not the only approach to understanding how to play the major scale over the whole neck. There are others. One of the most popular approaches outside of the five box patterns is the Three-Notes-Per-String approach. In this approach, we'll start on the root (in this case C), and play three notes on each string, until we've played two full octaves. Due to the nature of this approach, it is best to learn it starting with the root either on string 5 or string 6; that way you can cover a great number of possibilities without overthinking it.

We'll begin this approach by learning the root 6 pattern first. (This means the root of the scale is found on the 6th string.) The root 5 pattern will be covered later in this unit. Follow the chart just like you would the other charts presented in earlier units.

Fingerings for the Three-Note-Per-String Pattern:

String #	Index/Finger 1	Middle/Finger 2	Ring/Finger 3	Pinky/Finger 4
6	Fret 8 (Root Note)	Fret 10	--	Fret 12
5	Fret 8	Fret 10	--	Fret 12
4	Fret 9	Fret 10	--	Fret 12
3	Fret 9	Fret 10	--	Fret 12
2	Fret 10	--	Fret 12	Fret 13
1	Fret 10	--	Fret 12	Fret 13

Root 6 Three Notes Per String

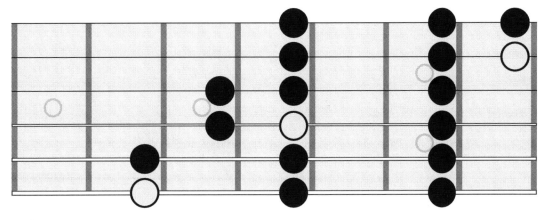

7th Fret

How to Play Warm-Ups #104, #105, and #106

Use the following warm-ups to learn how to play the C major scale using the three-notes-per-string approach. Just like the previous unit, only the eighth note examples are provided, so be sure to also practice them using quarter notes and sixteenth notes.

Start each warm-up at 60bpm on your metronome and gradually work up to around 120bpm.

Warm-Up #104

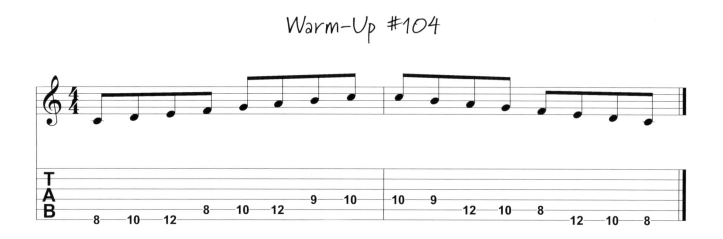

Warm-Up #105

In this warm-up from the same pattern, play the C major scale in the next higher octave.

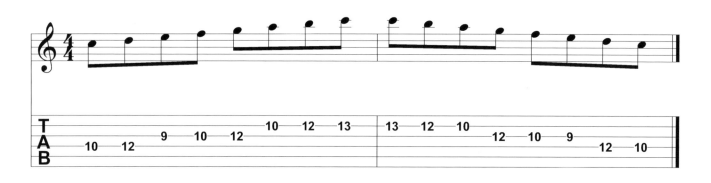

Warm-Up #106

The following pattern contains both octaves plus three additional diatonic notes that happen to fall on the first string.

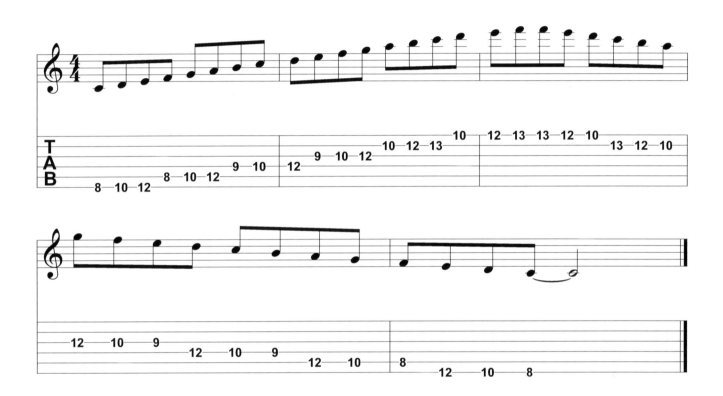

How to Play Warm-Up #107

This warm-up gives you a chance to play this new pattern using thirds. Be sure to set your metronome for 60bpm to start and slowly work up speed until you are able to play it comfortably around 120bpm.

Again, only the eighth note version of this warm-up has been written out. Be sure to also practice this same exercise with quarter notes and sixteenth notes.

Warm-Up #107

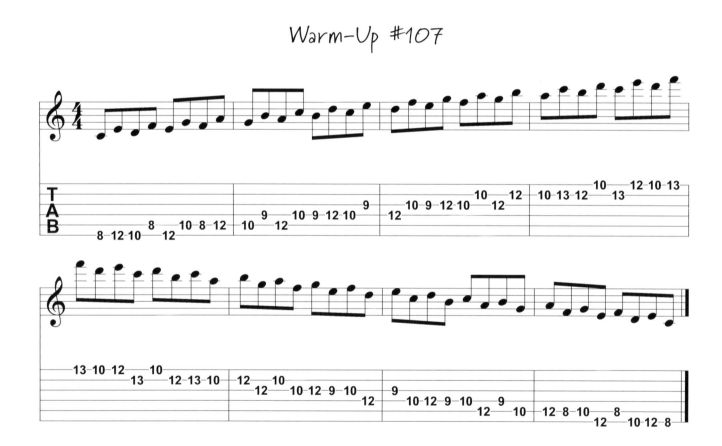

How to Play Warm-Up #108

Now we move on to fourths for this warm-up. So set your metronome for 60bpm to start and slowly work up speed until you are able to play it comfortably around 120bpm.

As before, only the eighth note version of this warm-up has been written out. Be sure to also practice this same exercise with quarter notes and sixteenth notes.

Warm-Up #108

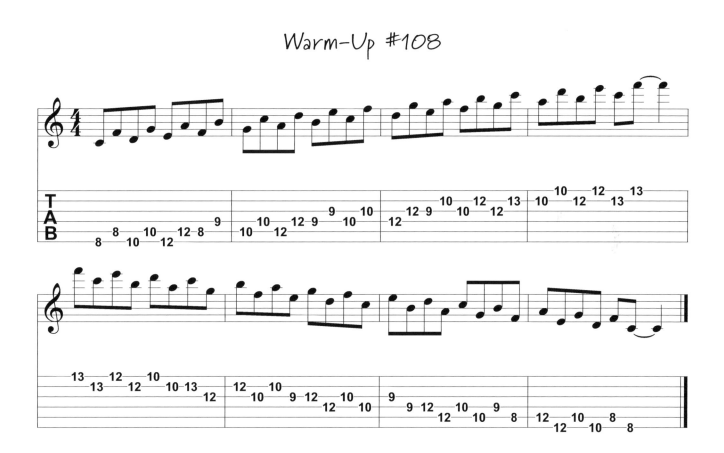

How to Play Warm-Up #109

Next up: play though the C major scale in fifths. Don't forget to set your metronome for 60bpm to start and slowly work up speed until you are able to play it comfortably around 120bpm.

Continue to practice this warm-up with quarter notes and sixteenth notes as you have been so far in this unit.

Warm-Up #109

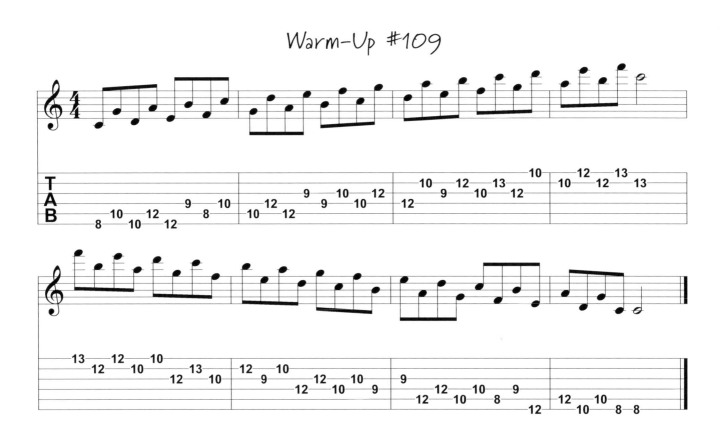

How to Play Warm-Up #110

For this warm-up, we are back to triplets, playing three notes up the scale and then on note back. Set your metronome for 60bpm to start and slowly work up speed until you are able to play it comfortably around 120bpm. And remember, for triplets it's one click for every three notes played. Continue to practice this warm-up with quarter notes and eighth notes.

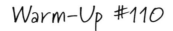

Warm-Up #110

143

Arpeggio Exercises

Practice the following arpeggio exercises. Chord symbols have been included so that you can relate the notes from each chord to their arpeggio. Play it first as quarter notes, then try the same exercise as eighth notes, then sixteenth notes. Be sure to use the metronome. Start each warm-up at 60bpm and gradually work up to around 120bpm.

Arpeggio Exercise #17

144

Arpeggio Exercise #17 (continued)

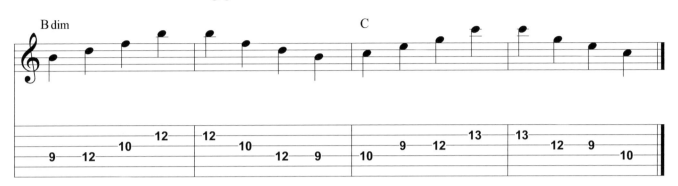

Arpeggio Exercise #18

This exercise includes additional arpeggios that can be played in this region of the neck. They are simply an octave higher than the ones found in Arpeggio Exercise #17.

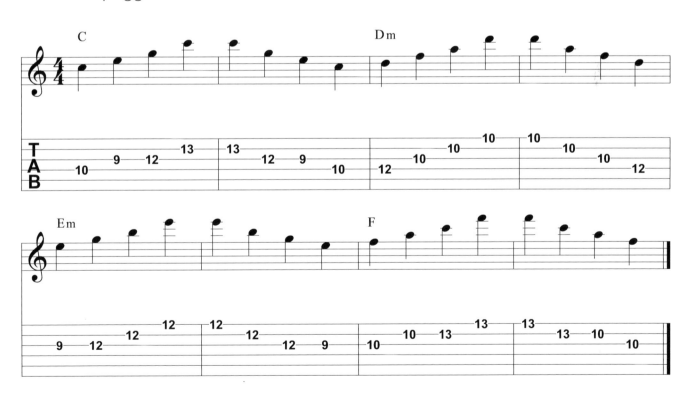

Major Scale Licks

The following licks are based on the three-notes-per-string pattern.

Begin by setting the metronome at 60bpm and gradually work up to around 120-130bpm for each lick.

Lick #31

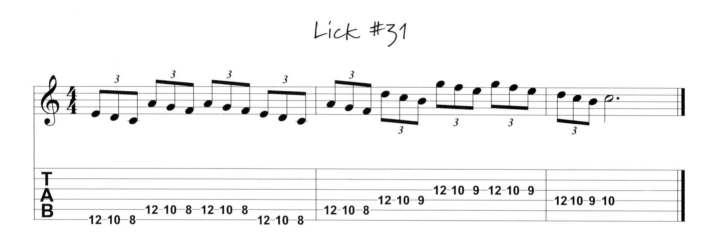

Lick #32

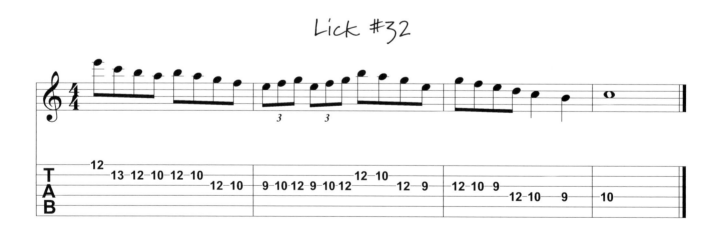

Lick #33

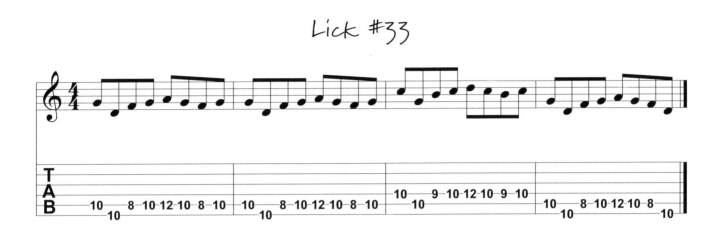

Lick #34

Lick #35

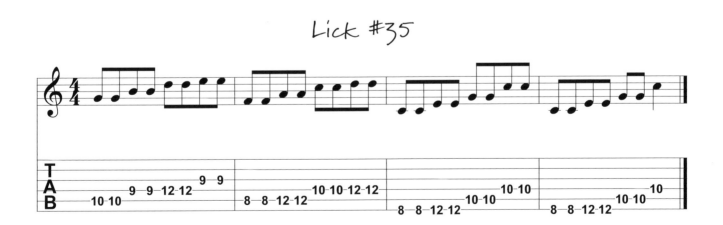

Root 5 Three Notes Per String

Next, we will explore the three-notes-per-string idea, but this time the root will be found on the fifth string, which means we'll have extra diatonic notes on the sixth string that will be included as well. For the key of C, the root can be found on the fifth string, third fret. The pattern extends all the way to the first string eighth fret. When descending you'll pass the root, play three lower notes on string six before returning to the root.

(See chart on the next page)

Fingerings for the Three-Note-Per-String Pattern:

String #	Index/Finger 1	Middle/Finger 2	Ring/Finger 3	Pinky/Finger 4
6	Fret 3	Fret 5	--	Fret 7
5	Fret 3	Fret 5	--	Fret 7
4	Fret 3	Fret 5	--	Fret 7
3	Fret 4	Fret 5	--	Fret 7
2	Fret 5	Fret 6	--	Fret 8
1	Fret 5	--	Fret 7	Fret 8

Root 5 Three Notes Per String Pattern

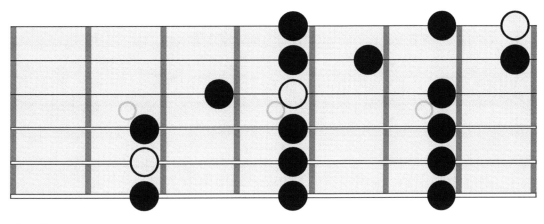

2nd Fret

Warm-Up #111

The following warm-up goes through only one of the octaves found in the pattern shown above. To start, place your index finger on the third fret of string five. Be sure to use the fingerings found on the previous page. As always, set your metronome for 60bpm and work your way up to 120bpm. Since the warm-up is presented as eighth notes, be sure to also try it out as quarter notes and sixteenth notes.

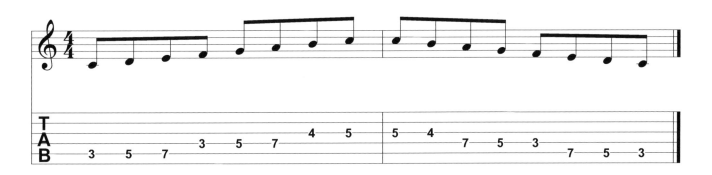

Warm-Up #112

This warm-up uses the higher octave found in the pattern. To start, place your index finger on the fifth fret of the third string, which is different from the fingerings suggested at the beginning of this section. Then use your ring finger for the seventh fret. After that, the fingerings will be the same as before. Set your metronome for 60bpm and work your way up to 120bpm. Since the warm-up is presented as eighth notes, be sure to try it out as quarter notes and sixteenth notes.

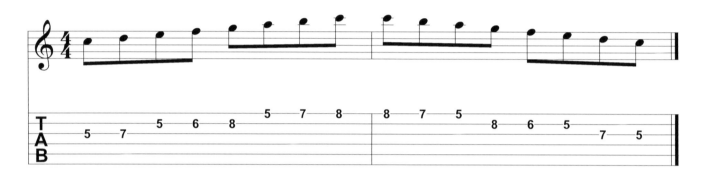

Warm-Up #113

Warm-up #113 contains both full octaves plus the lower diatonic notes available in this pattern. Use this section's suggested fingerings. Be sure to set your metronome for 60bpm and work up to 120bpm. Since the warm-up is presented as eighth notes, be sure to try it out as quarter notes and sixteenth notes.

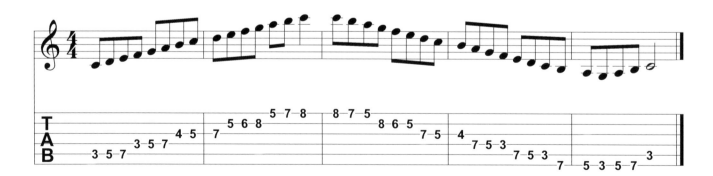

Warm-Up #114

Warm-up #114 moves through the whole pattern in thirds. Use this section's suggested fingerings. Set your metronome for 60bpm and work up to 120bpm. Since the warm-up is presented as eighth notes, be sure to try it out as quarter notes and sixteenth notes.

Warm-Up #115

Warm-up #115 moves through the whole pattern in fourths. Use this section's suggested fingerings. Set your metronome for 60bpm and work up to 120bpm. Since the warm-up is presented as eighth notes, be sure to try it out as quarter notes and sixteenth notes.

Warm-Up #116

Warm-up #116 has you practice the pattern in fifths. Use this section's suggested fingerings. Set your metronome for 60bpm and work up to 120bpm. Since the warm-up is presented as eighth notes, be sure to try it out as quarter notes and sixteenth notes.

Warm-Up #117

Warm-up #117 has you practicing the pattern in triplets, going up three notes and then back one. Use this section's suggested fingerings. Set your metronome for 60bpm and work up to 120bpm.

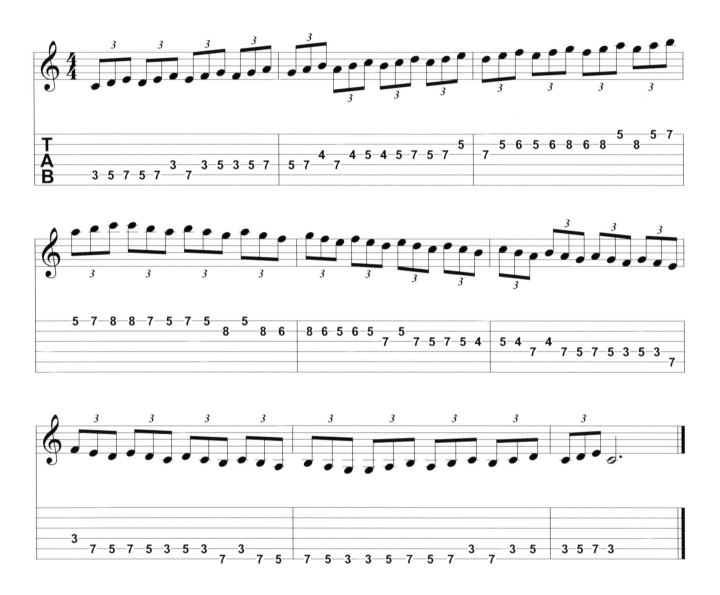

Arpeggio Exercise

Practice the following arpeggio exercise. Chord symbols have been included so that you can relate the notes from each chord to their arpeggio. Play it first as quarter notes. Then try the same exercise as eighth notes, then sixteenth notes. Be sure to use the metronome. Start the warm-up at 60bpm and gradually work up to around 120bpm.

Arpeggio Exercise #19

Arpeggio Exercise #19 (continued)

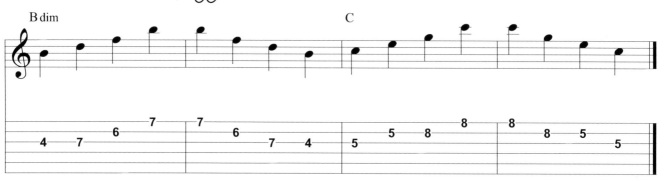

Major Scale Licks

The following licks are based on the three-notes-per-string pattern with the root on string 5. It is designed to help you practice the scale in a more musical fashion, rather than simply playing through the scale in a predetermined order.

Begin by setting the metronome at 60bpm and gradually work up to around 120-130bpm for each lick.

Lick #36

Lick #37

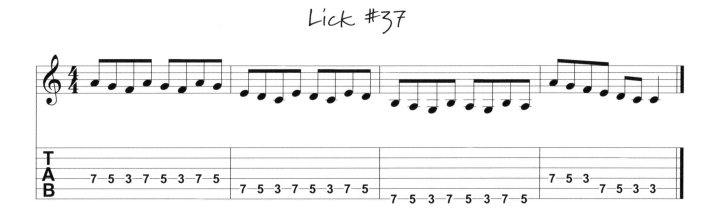

Lick #38

Lick #39

Lick #40

Unit 9

Changing Keys

Unit 9: How to Change Keys

Throughout this book, you have learned to play the major scale in the key of C. However, as you may already know, there are a total of 12 major keys. The roots of the scale were shown in each section of the book using gray dots on the scale charts. The root note is the name of the key, so if the key is C, the root note is C. Therefore, to change keys, simply find the new root note and play the pattern that goes with it.

For example, let's say you want to change from the key of C to the key of G using pattern 4 found in Unit 5 (see chart). The root in this pattern is also its lowest note (making it easier to move to a new key). The pattern starts on the eighth fret, which is the note C. The note G can be found on the third fret of the sixth string. Therefore, to play G major, simply move the pattern down to the third fret.

To change keys:

1. Identify the root notes. Find the root note you already know (C).

2. Locate the root note of the next key. (You will either need to know where the notes are located or use a root finder chart, like the one on page 165.)

3. Using the exact same pattern that worked for the original key, play the new key using that pattern.

4. Once you know where one of the five patterns can be found for the new key, all the other patterns change relative to that pattern. For example, in the key of C, Pattern 4 starts on the eighth fret, and Pattern 5 starts on the tenth fret. Then when it is moved to G, Pattern 4 starts on the third fret, and Pattern 5 will start on the fifth fret. Therefore, the patterns always connect together in same manner regardless of key. (See the G Major Scale Example on page 160.)

Example: Changing from C Major to G Major

Key of C Major

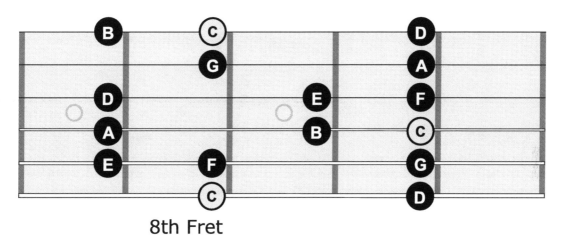

8th Fret

Key of G Major

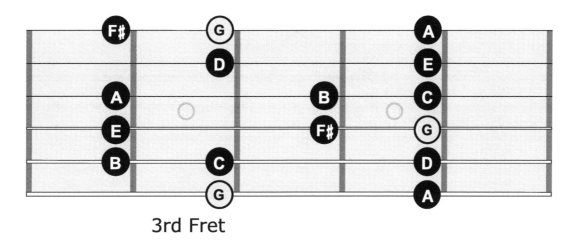

3rd Fret

Example: All G Major Scale Patterns

Note: Pattern 3 is shown below in both octaves

Pattern 1

Pattern 2

Pattern 3

Pattern 4

Pattern 5

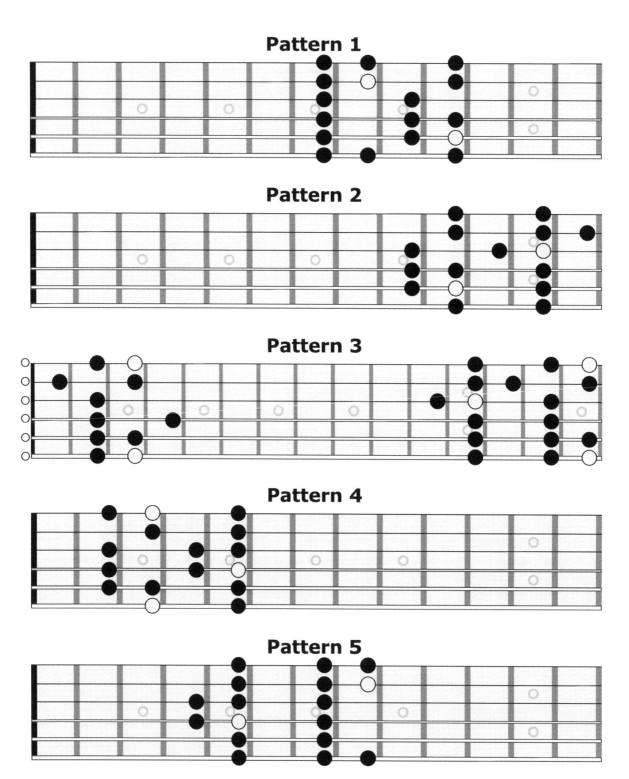

Example Key Change Warm-Ups

Warm-Up #118

Key of C Pattern 4

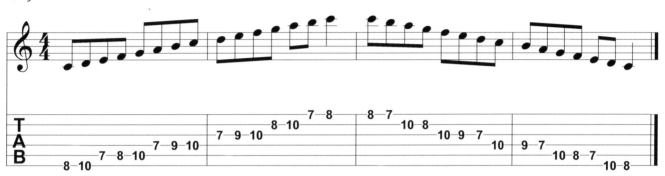

Key of G Pattern 4

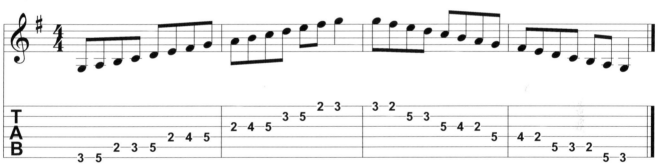

Key of F Pattern 4

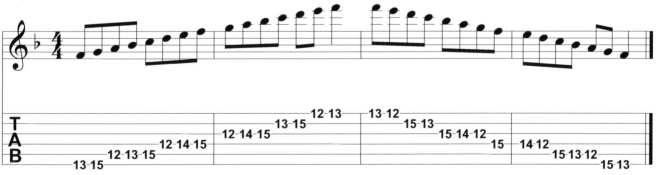

What's Next?

Now that you have an idea of how to change keys using the box patterns, you should be able to figure out how to play in all 12 keys! It just takes time and practice. The best thing you can do is to use the patterns shown in this book and apply them to every key. So you would play the pattern itself, followed by the pattern in thirds, fourths, fifths, and then play the licks and arpeggios in different keys as well.

The key change concept also applies to the Three-Note-Per-String approach. All you need to do is find your root and apply the patterns!

Once you have a strong grasp on the major scale and their keys, be sure to write your own melodies, licks, and riffs to help you find new sounds while continuing to master the major scale.

Root Finder Chart

The next page shows you where to find the root notes on the last three strings. Note the enharmonic spellings of the sharps and flats. Don't forget that G♯ = A♭ etc.

Root Finder Chart

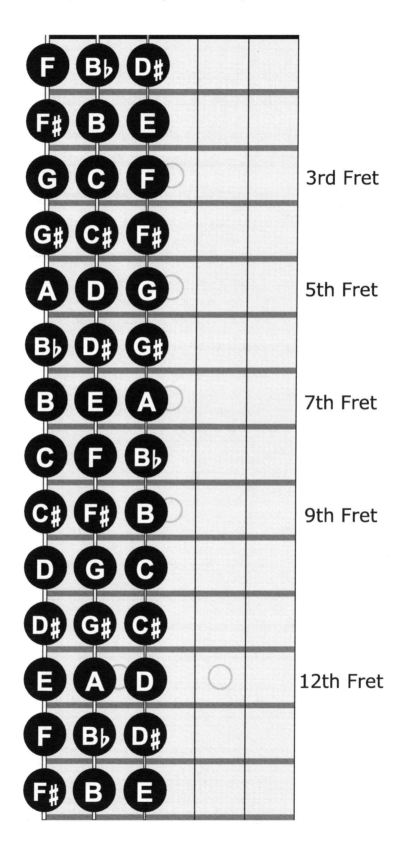

3rd Fret

5th Fret

7th Fret

9th Fret

12th Fret

Appendix

- How to Tune Your Guitar
- Introduction to Tablature
- Introduction to Reading Guitar Music
- How to Use a Metronome
- Major Scale Reference Chart

How to Tune Your Guitar

 The first thing you need to know in order to tune the guitar is what notes to tune to. The chart below shows the pitches of each string. Of course, if you are playing left-handed, these are reversed.

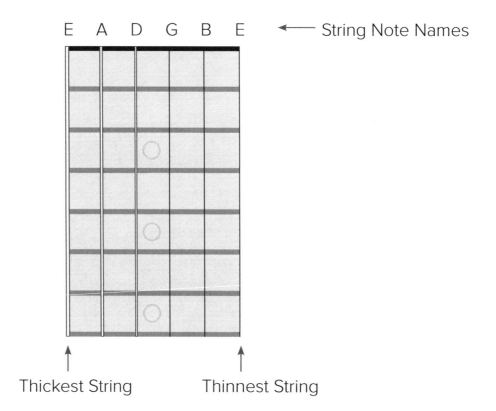

E   A   D   G   B   E   ◄——— String Note Names

↑ Thickest String   ↑ Thinnest String

There are a couple of sayings that can help you remember the names of the strings, from thick to thin:

Eddie **A**te **D**ynamite, **G**ood **B**ye **E**ddie.

Or the less violent:

Every **A**mateur **D**oes **G**et **B**etter **E**ventually.

2 The second thing you should know is that tuning takes practice. It can be a little frustrating at first, but once you've done it a few times it gets easier and easier.

3 The third thing you need to know is that most of the time your guitar will only need slight adjustments. Once it's in tune, it will usually stay fairly close to in tune most of the time. However, it is recommended that you check your tuning every time you pick up the guitar. Be sure to listen carefully to the sound of an in-tune guitar so you become familiar with what it should sound like.

4 Now that you know this, we can begin tuning the guitar. There are several tuning methods. The best method is to buy a guitar tuner and learn how to use it. (You can find information on tuners on the next page.)

Typically, most tuners will show which note you are playing and then tell you whether or not the note is too low, too high, or in tune. Usually, a meter of some kind will display this information.

If the string is too low, you'll want to tighten the string, If the string is too high, you'll want to loosen it. Be sure to listen to the sound of the string as well. Your ear will help you figure out if you are going too far from the in-tune note.

Guitar Tuners and Other Tuning Resources

Tuners come in all shapes and sizes. There are credit card sized tuners, apps, and clip-on tuners that attach to your guitar. There are also good tuning apps available, and many of them are free.

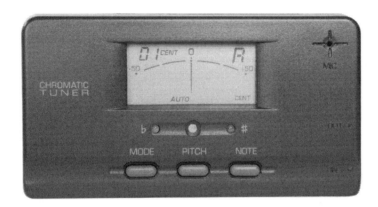

Another way you can tune the guitar is to use a reference pitch from an instrument that is already in tune. Most people use a piano, another in-tune guitar, or a pitch pipe to achieve this. In this case, you simply listen to the reference pitch and then match that pitch on your instrument. This can be difficult for beginners, but can help you to develop a strong ear as well as help you to develop your overall musicianship.

For more information on tuning, be sure to check out The Missing Method YouTube channel. There you will find video tutorials on how to tune your guitar as well as how to keep your guitar in tune.

Find it at: https://bit.ly/Missing-Method-YouTube

How to Read Tablature

Tablature (or TAB) is the most popular way of learning new songs. It is almost as old as standard notation for stringed instruments. The advantages of TAB are that it's easy to read and allows you to figure out songs much faster than standard notation. However, there are some drawbacks. Most TABS do not include any rhythm, meaning you have to either know how the song is supposed to sound ahead of time or rely on the standard notation, when available.

Tablature shows you *where* to play, while standard notation shows you *what* to play. Therefore, both are equally as valuable when learning a new song.

To read tablature, you should first know that each line represents a string on the guitar. The lowest string represents the bottom line, and the highest string is the top line. (See below.) Numbers are placed on the lines to show you on which fret or frets to place your fingers. For example, if you see a number 1 on the first string (the top line), simply play the first fret on the first string. A zero tells you to play the open string.

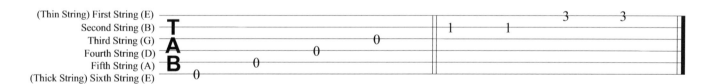

When reading tablature, the numbers on the lines represent the fret numbers.

The Elements of Reading Music

The Staff

Long ago there was no universal system to keep track of what a song sounded like. For a very long time, the only way to have a record of a song or piece of music was to pass it on from musician to musician by ear. Eventually, someone decided to place a circle on a line and call it a specific pitch. After some time, more lines were included, and the modern staff was born. The **staff** is simply a chart showing the highness and lowness of pitches. The lower a dot (or notehead) is on the staff, the lower the sound and vice versa.

In order to know which range of pitches to perform, clefs were used. A **clef** is a symbol that tells what notes to expect on the staff. There are several clefs in music, but for guitar we only need to learn one: the **treble clef**. (Though it is recommended to learn bass clef as well in order to develop your overall musicianship.)

Staff with Treble Clef

The treble clef tells you what specific notes, or pitches, you can expect to find on its lines and spaces. The lines are (from low to high): E G B D F. The spaces are F A C E. Many elementary schools teach a mnemonic device to help you remember these note names: Every Good Boy Does Fine. And of course the spaces spell FACE.

Ledger Lines

It is possible to go higher and lower than what is on the clef. When this is done, the extra notes are placed on lines called **ledger lines.**

In music there are a total of 12 notes that can occur at different pitch levels. Each different sound is given a letter name. Thus the musical alphabet consists of A B C D E F G. However, this represents only seven of these notes; the remaining five notes fall in between these and are designated either sharp or flat .

Understanding Time

The staff is divided up into sections called **bars** or **measures**. This is done to make the music easier to read and to help you figure out when to play the notes.

Each measure is only allowed a certain number of notes. This limitation allows us to keep track of time. The grouping of these notes is called **meter**. The most common meter is four beats per measure, or **4/4 time**.

Beat is the underlying current of the music. You don't necessarily hear the beat. Think of it as a second hand on a clock, a constant steady clicking that helps you keep track of time.

What you actually play is **rhythm**. Rhythm tells you how long or how short a pitch should be held. For example, in 4/4 time a whole note is sustained for four beats. A half note is sustained for two beats. A quarter note (which takes up a quarter of a measure) is sustained for only one beat.

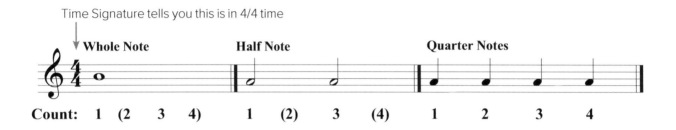

Besides 4/4 time, the second most common meter is 3/4. This means that there are only three beats per measure, instead of four, and the quarter note still represents the beat.

Eighth Notes

A quarter note can be further broken down into two eighth notes, each representing half a beat. When performing eighth notes, pick down on the downbeat, and up on the second half of each eighth note pair.

Eighth Notes

1 & 2 & 3 & 4 & 1 & 2 & 3 & 4 &

Sixteenth Notes

Eighth notes can be further broken down into four equal parts called sixteenth notes. That means that you can now play four notes for each beat. Just like eighth notes, sixteenth notes are often played using alternate picking. When counting sixteenth notes they are pronounced like this: One Eee And Uh, Two Eee and Uh, etc.

1 e & a 2 e & a 3 e & a 4 e & a

If you'd like to learn more about note reading, check out The Missing Method for Guitar Note Reading Series. With ample instruction and practice exercises, you'll master every note on the fretboard, in every key!

Keeping Time: How to Use Your Metronome

When you are first starting any instrument, practicing with a metronome can seem frustrating or even impossible at times. The fact of the matter is that it is something you'll want to get good at and *can* once you know how. One obstacle, however, can be physical movement. For some, it won't yet be possible to move fast enough to lock in with the metronome. But don't worry; with practice and time you'll be able to use the metronome without any trouble.

There are many different types of metronomes out there, from the traditional wind-up, piano top metronome, to apps for your phone or tablet. They all work well and do about the same thing. Their purpose to provide the beat for you.

Step One: Synchronize with the Metronome

To start using the metronome, turn it on and select a relatively slow beat. I recommend somewhere around 50 beats per minute (bpm). Before you do anything, listen to the beat. Then begin by tapping your foot along with the beat. Be sure to anticipate each beat and play with the metronome. Don't wait for the click then tap your foot. Tap in sync with it.

Once you feel in sync with the metronome, begin to count out loud along with the clicks: 1, 2, 3, 4, over and over again. Keep your foot tapping while you do this. Feel the pulse; feel your footfalls; feel the time, and lock in.

Stop the metronome, but keep tapping at the same rate of speed. After about 30 seconds, turn the metronome back on to see how close you've come. Chances are you will have either sped up or slowed down. That's normal. Everyone has a different heart rate, and this can affect your perception of time. But with practice, you'll start to feel different tempos and different meters.

Step Two: Practice with the Metronome

Once you feel comfortable with step one, pick up your guitar and take some time to get in sync with the metronome. To do this, choose any open string and play this string while you tap your foot, listen to the click, and count out loud.

Next, try it with any chord. Simply tap your foot with the metronome clicking while you strum.

After that, take any song or exercise and play only the first full phrase or measure; that way you can focus on the time more so than on the pitches. After one phrase or measure is complete, move on to the next one, repeating the process. Once you have a couple of phrases or measures down with the metronome, turn it off again and try playing just as accurately without it.

The key here is that you DON'T want to try and play an entire song with the metronome yet. Instead, use it to help you focus your practicing of small sections, so you can play them more accurately.

Keep in mind that even seasoned professionals still use metronomes to practice. It's the best way to help you focus on your timing, which is crucial for playing with others, as well as sounding your best overall. Time is often overlooked by new players since the early focus is on the right notes, chords, or just getting your fingers in the right spots. But once you have all that, you have to be aware of and practice your timing.

 Like tuners, metronomes can be found in a variety of shapes, sizes, and formats, including downloadable apps.

177

Quick Reference Scale Charts

Pattern 1

Pattern 2

Pattern 3

Pattern 4

Pattern 5

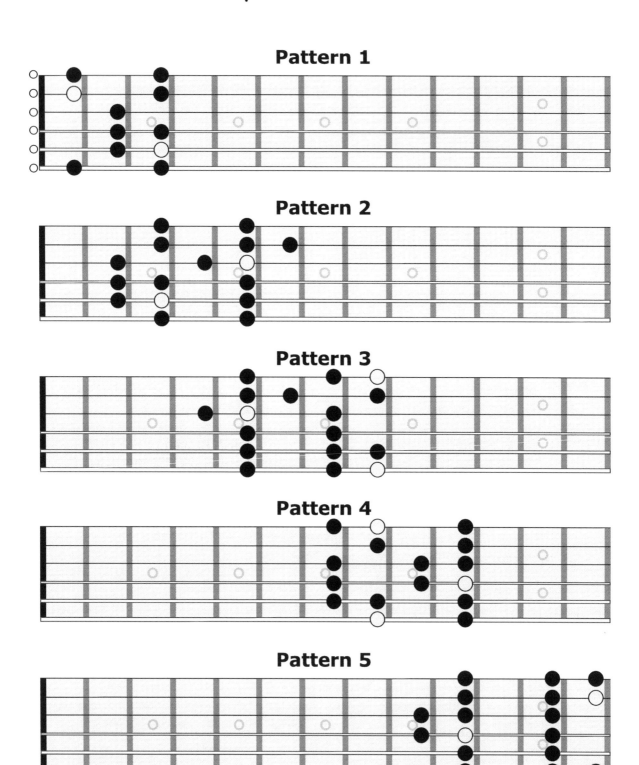

Pattern 1 (One Octave Higher)

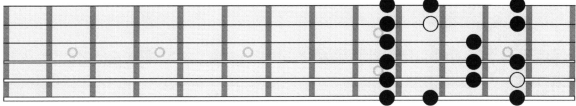

Fret 4

Fret 12

Three Notes Per String

Root 6

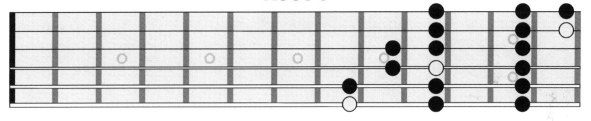

Root 5

Resources to Help You Take Your Playing Further

Technique Master

When it comes to playing any instrument, developing strong technique can make all the difference. Build coordination, avoid injury, increase your speed and accuracy, improve your picking skills, and improve your timing with *Technique Master*.

Pentatonic Master

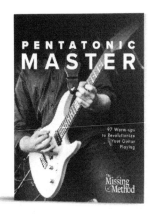

Every guitar player needs to know the pentatonic scale. It's as important to the guitar as learning chords, and countless numbers of songs and genres have used it as the basis for riffs, licks, and solos. Now, with *Pentatonic Master* you can master the scale all over the neck while you warm-up!

Perfect Practice

Rethink how you practice and get out of a practicing rut with *Perfect Practice*. Learn the secrets to transforming your practice time into time well-spent. This book will help you figure out how to identify and overcome obstacles in your way by showing you what to practice and how to structure your time to get results faster!

Guitar Chord Master™ Series

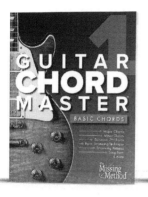  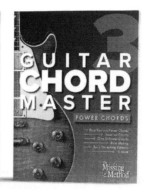

Guitar Chord Master is the only method book series that focuses exclusively on learning chords and strum patterns. Each book takes you step-by-step through the process of learning chords in a musical context, allowing you to master them for life! The series covers open chords, power chords, barre chords, how to use a capo, moveable shapes, and much more. Available in right and left-handed editions.

The Missing Method for Guitar Note Reading Series

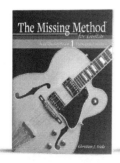 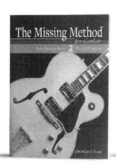 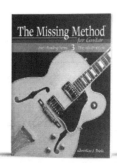  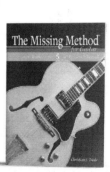

Unlock your musicianship and gain a new level of expertise with The Missing Method for Guitar Note Reading series. You'll learn to read every note on the guitar, from the open strings to the 22nd fret. If you are looking to master the fretboard, this is the series for you! Available in right and left-handed editions.

Find these and more at TheMissingMethod.com.

Made in the USA
Las Vegas, NV
20 March 2023

69379365R00103